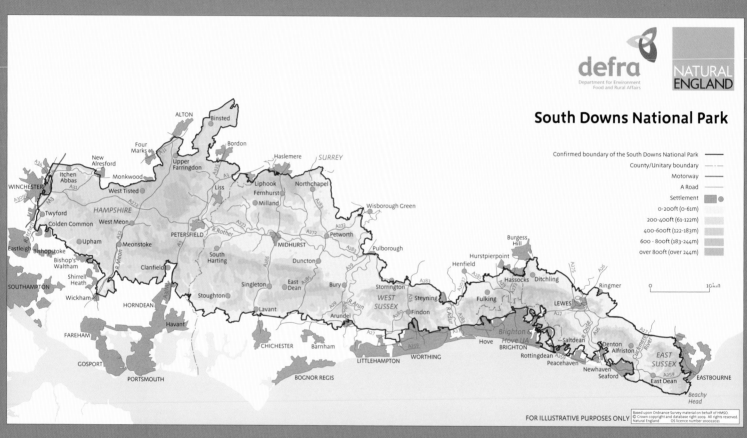

Map showing the boundary of the National Park, principal towns and height above sea level. (Reproduced by courtesy of Natural England.)

The Natural History
of the
South Downs National Park

by Robin Crane and Rendel Williams

ISBN 978-0-904973-23-5

Published by The Sussex Archaeological Society, Lewes

Designed and typeset by Dora A. Kemp, MPhil

Printed in Great Britain by Short Run Press, Exeter

Contents

© Ian Seccombe

Looking south-west towards the Ouse valley from the Lewes Downs.

Preface

This book has been written with the object of stimulating people's interest in the wildlife and countryside of the South Downs National Park, not simply by highlighting some special plants and animals, but by giving readers a greater understanding of the evolution of the wild places, the history of nature conservation and the management of habitats and species.

The plant and animal life within the National Park is both rich and diverse. It would be an impossible task to cover every aspect of the biodiversity within the confines of this book. We have therefore set out to paint the broad picture, to describe the features that make this area so special and to highlight some of the best places to explore.

For those who wish to embark upon a closer study of our flora and fauna we have listed the key organisations which are involved in the recording and conservation of wildlife within the National Park, together with their contact details.

Note: a definition of the Weald

Historically, references to the Weald have been used in different ways and need some clarification. 'Andredsweald' is the word the Anglo-Saxons used to describe the great forests lying between the chalk hills of the North and the South Downs. Although some writers, such as the authors of the New Naturalist book *The Weald*, include the chalk of the North and South Downs in the Weald, we use the term as defined by William Topley in his highly influential *Geology of the Weald* (1875). He clearly understood the Weald to be the outcrops of sandstone, clay and other strata (all pre chalk in age) located between the North and South Downs, bounded on the east by the English Channel and on the west by the unnamed range of chalk hills in West Sussex and Hampshire that runs by Selborne and Noar Hill.

Acknowledgements

We unhesitatingly wish to dedicate this book to the late Dr. Francis Rose, who was regarded as one of the finest botanists in Europe and undertook much of his work within the area that has become the South Downs National Park. He was closely involved in the initial designations of many of the protected sites within the Park. All his detailed records, compiled over many decades, are now held by the Sussex Biodiversity Record Centre.

We are most grateful to Mike Edwards, Martin Willing and Graeme Lyons for giving us advice on heathland invertebrates, molluscs and woodland invertebrates, respectively. The staff of the Hampshire & Isle of Wight Wildlife Trust, the Sussex Wildlife Trust, the Hampshire Biological Information Centre and the Sussex Biodiversity Record Centre provided us with much useful data and advice. Both Wildlife Trusts were extremely helpful in offering many of the superb photographs from their libraries, which were mostly taken by volunteers and given to their Trusts to use in support of nature conservation. Professional wildlife photographers and others have also generously provided illustrative material.

We are indebted to Michael Packard for supplying the geological map and to Tim Aspen for revising its National Park boundary. We are also grateful to Frances Abraham, Tony Whitbread and Phil Belden for reading an early draft text, correcting our errors and offering us their constructive criticisms. John Manley and Robin Milner-Gulland have provided invaluable support as editors throughout the preparation of this book. Finally, our special thanks are due to Dora Kemp for designing all the page layouts and for assisting with final copy editing.

Robin Crane and Rendel Williams
May 2013

Some special South Downs National Park species

Round-headed Rampion

This eye-catching plant, which only grows on chalk grasslands in a few areas of southern England, has its stronghold in the South Downs National Park. It is popularly known as 'Pride of Sussex' but is also found on some of the best Hampshire downland nature reserves. Its distinctive globular head is not a single flower, but a collection of small flowers. It flowers in July and August and favours warm, shallow soils.

© Roger Wilmshurst

Stone Curlew

The extraordinary and charismatic Stone Curlew is one of Britain's rarest and most threatened birds. Having been lost as a breeding species on the South Downs, it made a welcome return in 2007 to West Sussex where it now breeds in very small numbers, carefully protected by the RSPB with the essential support of sympathetic landowners. To date Stone Curlew have not re-colonised the Hampshire Downs in the National Park, although several pairs are now well established further west of Winchester.

Adonis Blue - Ant and Butterfly

The spectacular Adonis Blue butterfly is strictly confined to chalk downland and survives only at a scattering of sites in southern England. The unmistakably brilliant colour of the male, with black lines across its white wing margins, contrasts with the chocolate brown female. The butterfly is found only on south-facing hillsides where there is closely grazed turf and its larval foodplant, Horseshoe Vetch grows. It is on the wing in May and June with a second brood appearing in August and September.

Nearly all the species of blue butterflies have a special relationship with particular species of ants. The ants feed on a sugary substance secreted from a gland on the Blues' caterpillars and in return they guard them, helping to ward off potential predators and parasites. At night the ants sometimes cover the Adonis Blue caterpillars loosely in earth. When the caterpillars pupate, the ants constantly attend the pupae, some of which end up actually in the ants' nests. Like other species of our blue butterflies, the caterpillars and the pupae 'sing', presumably to stimulate the ants. Without the beneficial 'farming' activities of the ants, it is impossible to sustain a population of Adonis Blue butterflies.

© Martin Willing

Cheese Snail

The attractive little Cheese Snail has a flattened shell resembling a rounded cheddar cheese, which accounts for its English name. It is mainly a central European species and is rare or absent in much of western France. The English populations form an isolated pocket at the extreme north-western end of this range and are restricted to woods on the chalk of the South Downs and East Hampshire. All but one of these populations live within the new South Downs National Park. The sole exception lies just west of the Park boundary.

© Graeme Lyons/Sussex Wildlife Trust

Wart-biter Bush Cricket

This cricket has its largest population in Britain at Castle Hill National Nature Reserve near Brighton. Its weird name comes from the belief that it can cure human warts. It can nip when roughly handled but is generally docile as well as being remarkably elusive. In southern England it is at the extreme north-western edge of its European range.

Geology of the South Downs National Park

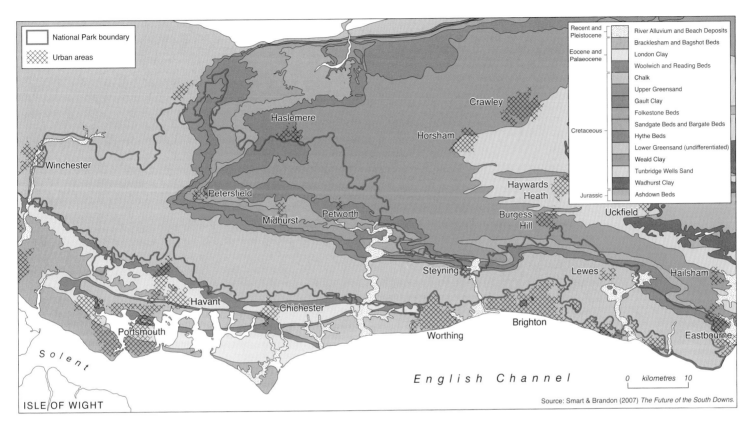

National Park boundary

Urban areas

Recent and Pleistocene		River Alluvium and Beach Deposits
Eocene and Palaeocene		Bracklesham and Bagshot Beds
		London Clay
		Woolwich and Reading Beds
Cretaceous		Chalk
		Upper Greensand
		Gault Clay
		Folkestone Beds
		Sandgate Beds and Bargate Beds
		Hythe Beds
		Lower Greensand (undifferentiated)
		Weald Clay
		Tunbridge Wells Sand
		Wadhurst Clay
Jurassic		Ashdown Beds

0   kilometres   10

Source: Smart & Brandon (2007) *The Future of the South Downs.*

The Chalk, which underlies much of the National Park, is relatively resistant to weathering and erosion, and gives rise to the relatively high ground of the South Downs. Younger sands, gravels and clays (Tertiary Beds) overlie the Chalk in places. Because the Chalk is highly permeable, even heavy rains rarely produce surface runoff and streams are generally absent.

Beneath the Chalk are the Upper Greensand and the Gault Clay, which outcrop along the base of the Chalk escarpment around the rim of the Weald. The Upper Greensand is a pale, often calcareous sandstone of no great thickness, and is largely absent from East Sussex. The Gault Clay is highly impermeable and almost everywhere forms low ground.

Still older than the Gault is the Lower Greensand, which in West Sussex is divided into the Hythe, Sandgate and Folkestone Beds. The Hythe Beds are represented by sands and sandstones with subordinate amounts of hard chert. They tend to form ridges, plateaus and escarpments. The Sandgate Beds are highly variable and have been eroded to form the valley of the West Sussex Rother. The Folkestone Beds are for the most part free-draining sands; their infertile soils give rise to some important areas of lowland heath.

Underlying the Lower Greensand is the Weald Clay, which occupies only a small area of the National Park, but within the Weald as a whole forms a wide horseshoe-shaped outcrop.

Heather in full bloom on Iping and Stedham Commons with the chalk downs on the horizon.

'It would be difficult to find anywhere in the world an area of comparable size which exhibits so perfectly the responses of plant, animal and human life to the stimuli of varied physical environments as the Weald.' Editors' preface to 'The Weald', *New Naturalist* no. 26.

The Natural History of the South Downs National Park

Nature and its Conservation in the South Downs National Park

In the north-west corner of the South Downs National Park is the remarkably unspoilt Hampshire village of Selborne. It was the parish of the Reverend Gilbert White, whose book 'The Natural History and Antiquities of Selborne' was first published in 1789 and has become the fourth most published book in the English language. It is acknowledged not only for White's remarkably acute observations on wildlife in their natural habitats, but also as a masterpiece of English literature. The publication is made up of a series of letters to his friends in which he describes such diverse subjects as the behaviour of migrating birds, the life-cycle of the Field Cricket and his identification of the Harvest Mouse and Chiffchaff as new species that had previously not been distinguished from their close relatives. His first letter describes the topography and the extraordinary variety of geology and soils in his locality that yielded such a wealth of flora and fauna for his study. Had he lived in a less diverse area his work might never have been published. It is this great variety in the underlying geology that gives rise to the many different habitats that make the South Downs National Park a paradise for naturalists today.

© Hugh Clark/Sussex Wildlife Trust

A Harvest Mouse supporting itself on an ear of wheat using its prehensile tail. Gilbert White was amazed by the round, compact nests that these mice construct.

The South Downs themselves are the chalk hills that form the spine of the National Park. They stretch from Beachy Head to Winchester, a distance of about 72 miles. In the east, Kipling's 'blunt, bow-headed whale-backed downs' with their deep cut coombes and denes are mostly tree-free landscapes formed through centuries of sheep grazing. Further west the Downs become much more wooded. Forming a dramatic edge to the Downs in Sussex is a high scarp slope that overlooks the sandstone ridges and clay lowlands. Away from the scarp the chalk strata dip gently away to the south. Throughout the length of 'these majestic mountains' as Gilbert White called them, one is always aware of the sea; from the dramatic sea cliffs in the east to the more gentle coastal plain in the west where one can often enjoy views of the Isle of Wight across the Solent.

The view northwards from the chalk escarpment at the National Trust's Harting Down near Petersfield is one of the finest in southern England. To the west lie the wooded Hampshire Hangers that eventually lead one to Selborne. To the north is a succession of sandstone ridges intersected by clay valleys that rise gradually to Black Down, at 280 m, the highest point of the South Downs National Park. On these Greensands are a series of wild heathlands. Much further east amidst the Weald Clay vales of the low Weald are remnant ancient woodlands, notably The Mens and Ebernoe Common. This western Weald area is distinctive for its thin strips of ancient woodlands and hedgerows known as 'shaws' or 'rews' that divide

many of the small fields – a landscape that remains little changed since mediaeval times. Another feature of the National Park is a series of river valleys and streams. In Hampshire there are the clear chalk waters of the Rivers Itchen and the Meon. The River Rother in the western Weald is the least altered and most natural river in the National Park. The Rivers Adur, Arun, Ouse and Cuckmere all rise north of the Park and have their own unique characteristics. The wetlands associated with some of them are of great importance for their wildlife, rivalling in some respects both the Norfolk Broads and the Somerset Levels.

Whilst the rich diversity of the wildlife in the National Park is largely attributable to the underlying geology, the biodiversity is further enhanced by the fact that the South Downs and the Weald lie at a transition between the oceanic climate of Britain and the warmer, drier, more continental climate of Europe. This gives rise to a unique mixture of flora and fauna, especially on the chalk downs, where the more southerly or continental species tend to be found on the warmer south-facing slopes while the more oceanic species favour the cooler and moister north-facing slopes.

Human impact on landscapes and wildlife

The wildlife habitats found in the National Park today had their origins in the natural forest that gradually covered the area after the last ice age ended about ten thousand years ago. This forest would have been immensely varied in character, not just the

dense impenetrable world of trees that some writers once imagined. Storms, erosion, flooding and burning, as well as the activities of large grazing animals, would have created a great variety of habitats, ranging from dense wooded forest to open grazed areas, marshes and bogs.

Human influence on the landscape began further back in time than once was generally believed. There is growing evidence that Mesolithic hunter-gatherers, perhaps as early as 8,000 years ago, deliberately used fire to create open areas in the forest on the Lower Greensand outcrop in West Sussex, either to make hunting easier or to promote the growth of Hazel, whose nuts were a key element in their diet. These interventions promoted the eventual development of heathland in the area, probably long before heaths came into being elsewhere.

With their light, well-drained soils the Downs were an obvious target for early settlers and they began to clear forests and create their first fields on the Chalk about 5000 years ago. Wheat, barley and oats were grown, and sheep and cattle were grazed in grassy areas. Over the years the farmers began to exploit new areas on heavier soils and adopt new techniques. In the river valleys and in the Weald the wetter pastures were grazed in spring and hay was cut in summer. Wood pastures were created where cattle could graze amongst the trees of the forests, and pigs could forage. Woodlanders felled mature trees for constructing buildings, and shrubs such as hazel were coppiced in rotation to produce fencing,

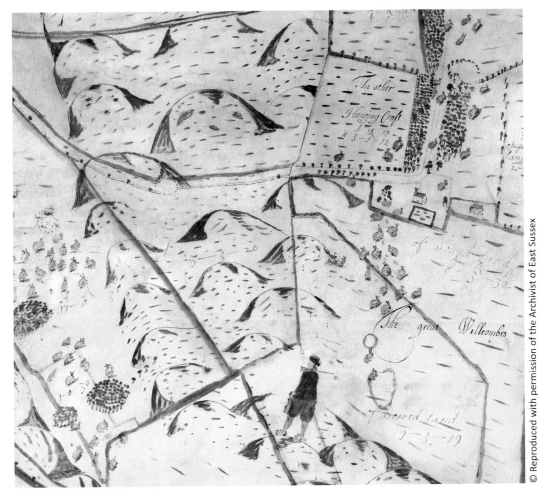

A warrener with his rabbits at Danny Place near Hurstpierpoint, 1666.

firewood and wattle for lining houses. Even the natural resources of the relatively barren heathlands were harvested.

In mediaeval times many of the richer landowners established enclosed deer parks, where they could hunt, undisturbed by the peasantry. European Rabbits, which were introduced into Britain by the Normans, were carefully tended in specially created warrens and for centuries were the preserve of noblemen. It was not until winter crops were planted and pheasant breeding became fashionable some two hundred years ago that escaped rabbits were able to establish a firm footing in the wild. With plenty of food available on farmland in hard times and many of their predators killed by gamekeepers, the population exploded and through sheer force of numbers they began to transform many wild plant communities.

Until the Industrial Revolution, people in Britain were largely dependent upon the natural resources of the countryside in their farming and forestry activities. The permanent pastures and hay meadows

© Ian Seccombe

During the Second World War the push to increase food supplies was aided by the introduction of new agricultural machinery, particularly the Fordson tractor. On the South Downs substantial tracts of land were ploughed for the first time in living memory.

boom and depression, particularly in the last two centuries. War-time food shortages encouraged farmers to put more land into cereal production, but the onset of peace and the availability of cheaper food from overseas suppliers all too often led to a dramatic fall in farm incomes and a flight from the land. As recently as the 1920s and 1930s some areas of chalk downland became uneconomic to farm and were abandoned. Over the last seventy years there have been revolutionary changes in agricultural practices and the impact of human activities upon our rich heritage of flora and fauna has been far greater than it had been in the previous five thousand.

The German strategy in the 1939–45 Battle of the Atlantic was to isolate Britain from its traditional supply routes, and the ruthless sinking of our merchant ships led to a serious shortage of food. The Government therefore mobilised every possible means of increasing food production at home. All available land that could be used to grow crops was ploughed up.

Other large areas of the South Downs were set aside for military training. Left unmanaged, much former sheep-grazed chalk grassland became overgrown with scrub and coarse grasses, and arable fields were also overwhelmed by grass and weeds. Rabbits were able to breed unchecked. As late as 1946–47 the farmland on Amberley Mount was still littered with spent ammunition and populated by vast hordes of rabbits which had honeycombed the hedgerow banks with their burrows.

remained rich in wild flowers and grasses. The woodlands that were coppiced in rotation had numerous open spaces where primroses, violets, bluebells and butterflies could flourish. Hedgerows were planted with native shrubs and these provided a haven for birds and insects. The intensive sheep grazing on the Downs created one of the richest of all our semi-natural habitats – herb-rich chalk grassland.

The landscapes of the South Downs National Park today have a quality of timelessness about them, as if they have existed for millennia. In fact they have been continuously modified in response to changing human needs in time of war and peace,

Wildlife catastrophe

It is not surprising that, after severe food shortages during the Second World War (1939–45), post-war Governments were determined to make Britain self-sufficient. They pursued policies that provided strong incentives for farmers to become even more productive.

Farmers, supported with generous subsidies, were able to take advantage of major technological advances in equipment and chemicals that dramatically increased their output but were disastrous for wildlife. More space was required to accommodate the large farm machinery and to increase the land under cultivation. With powerful heavyweight tractors, ancient hedgerows and copses could be effortlessly removed, creating bleak prairie-like landscapes.

The increasing use of fertilisers, herbicides and pesticides, which were liberally sprayed on crops or used for eliminating livestock pests, had a devastating effect on wild plants and animals. Toxic chemicals passed through the food chains, destroying seed-eating birds and eventually killing many birds-of-prey such as Buzzards and Peregrine Falcons, which suffered a devastating reduction in their numbers.

Fertilisers and pesticides that were washed off the fields by rain soon found their way into streams and rivers. The pesticides passed through the aquatic food chain and played a large part in the disappearance of the Otter from most of Britain. Run-off water carrying fertilisers and laced with herbicides turned ditches and dykes that were once rich in plants and insects into sterile lifeless drains. The enrichment of some ditches led to terrible algal blooms which were seriously destructive to other forms of life.

The impact of these modern farming methods in Sussex and Hampshire was greatest on the chalk downs. Vast swathes of the ancient chalk grasslands were converted to arable and intensive agriculture. The majority of the remaining ancient flower-rich chalk grasslands were on the steepest hillsides that had resisted the assaults of the modern tractor. Whilst many of these areas were no longer tended by sheep they were grazed by large numbers of rabbits, whose population had dramatically increased after the Second World War. The arrival of the Myxomatosis virus in Britain in 1953, almost certainly introduced by man, initially had a catastrophic impact on the rabbits, killing over 99% of the population. The subsequent lack of grazing led to the rich chalk turf being overwhelmed by coarse grasses and, eventually, by large areas of Hawthorn-dominated scrub. Many of the wild flowers that characterise the chalk disappeared whilst colonies of some chalkland butterflies such as the beautiful Adonis Blue were greatly reduced in number.

© Phil Belden

Prairie-like arable fields at Loose Bottom between Lewes and Brighton, 1983.

© Edward Reeves/Lewes

The same scene showing extensive chalk grasslands and gorse thickets, 1936.

In woodlands, traditional coppicing had long ceased to be economic except in a few areas specially planted with Sweet Chestnut. With no active management the neglected coppices grew to form canopies that prevented sunlight from reaching the plants on the ground. The Fritillary butterflies, whose caterpillars feed on violets and need the warmth of sunlight to survive, suffered a steady decline. The Pearl-bordered Fritillary, which was once very common in coppiced woodlands in Sussex, was reduced to just a few sites.

The heathlands were already suffering from neglect as traditional forms of management had become uneconomic. The situation was made worse when Government grants and tax incentives encouraged foresters to plant many heathlands with alien conifers which then shaded out the interesting species that are totally dependent upon the open habitats.

As the world became increasingly aware of the devastating impact of all these changes upon the environment, pressure from nature conservationists and the general public increased, and the fight to save our ever-dwindling inheritance of wildlife gathered momentum. It was a mission that had begun over a century ago.

The beautiful High Brown Fritillary was particularly badly hit when woodland management became less intensive and is now confined to just a few places in western Britain.

© Gillian Thompson

© Neil Hulme

Nature conservation

From the 17th Century onwards there was an increasing interest in the recording and cataloguing of Britain's native plant and animal life. Distinguished naturalists such as Gilbert White and Charles Darwin were inspired by the natural world and the South Downs were the focus of authors such as Richard Jefferies and W.H. Hudson, who wrote eloquently about the wildlife and special features of this iconic landscape. As access to the countryside gradually became easier with the introduction of trains, bicycles, cars and charabancs, many amateur naturalists were able to travel around and add to the growing knowledge of British flora and fauna. The collecting of plants, insects and birds' eggs became all the rage, but there were some visionaries whose main concern was to protect Britain's flora and fauna from what they saw as growing threats, not just from rapacious collectors, but also from changes in land management.

In 1912 Charles Rothschild founded the Society for the Promotion of Nature Reserves (SPNR). Its prime objective was to be the safeguarding of habitats. This was a new concept for naturalists in Britain, who had previously concentrated upon the conservation of a few rare species. Rothschild organised a survey to identify the finest wildlife sites and this led to 282 places in the UK and Ireland being labelled as worthy of conservation. This list included Amberley Wild Brooks, Kingley Vale, St Catherine's Hill and the Lewes Downs which are now in the South Downs National Park.

When the SPNR was founded it did not intend to own land itself, but to be an enabling society. It identified the recently formed National Trust as the best-equipped organisation to own and manage nature reserves, but after the First World War the Trust's support was not sustained as it did not wish to continue acquiring sites 'only of interest to the naturalist'. The fledgling RSPB was also a reluctant landowner, preferring to depend on 'watchers' policing sensitive areas. With few exceptions, little progress was made in establishing nature reserves until after the Second World War. However, there were strong campaigns to protect the rural countryside as a whole from the 1880s onwards. Eastbourne and Brighton Councils had particular foresight in acquiring large tracts of land on the South Downs to contain urban sprawl.

Fortunately, the SPNR came to life again during the Second World War. It drove the initiatives which eventually led, in 1949, to the creation of a national government agency for nature conservation known as The Nature Conservancy, which currently operates as part of Natural England. The Agency's responsibilities included the establishment and maintenance of nature reserves *'for the study of, and research into, matters relating to the fauna and flora of Great Britain'* and for the purpose of *'preserving flora, fauna or geological or physiographical features of special interest'*. The Agency used Rothschild's list of outstanding sites to provide the basis for the selection of its first National Nature Reserves (NNRs). From that list Kingley

Charles Rothschild in 1907.

Vale NNR was established in 1952, one of the earliest to be secured. Other National Nature Reserves designated by the Agency which are now in the South Downs National Park are Lewes Downs, Castle Hill, Lullington Heath and Ebernoe Common in Sussex and Butser Hill, Old Winchester Hill, Beacon Hill and Ashford Hangers in Hampshire.

In the 1960s the SPNR made a vital decision in providing the resources and leadership that led to the establishment of the network of local Wildlife Trusts which now cover the whole of the UK. The Hampshire & Isle of Wight Wildlife Trust and the Sussex Wildlife Trust were both founded

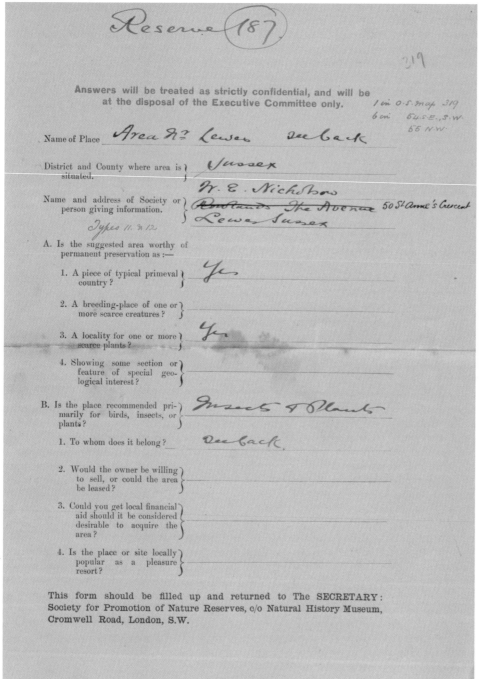

in 1961. Their prime purposes are to conserve and enhance the landscape, its wildlife and habitats and to build on their expertise to encourage people to enjoy, understand and take action to safeguard our natural heritage for current and future generations.

The Wildlife Trusts' greatest asset has been their local knowledge. This has enabled them to identify threats to wildlife habitats and species on their doorsteps at an early stage and to take appropriate action. Over the years they have established many first-class nature reserves, some of which were saved from imminent destruction. The Wildlife Trusts have also had a strong

The nomination for the Lewes Downs to be included in the Society for the Promotion of Nature Reserves' schedule of sites 'most worthy of permanent preservation'. It was added to 'Rothschild's list' in 1915. By 'Lewes Downs' the proposer, Mr. Nicholson, meant Malling Down and Cliffe Hill, the nearest chalk downs east of Lewes. The scarce plants and insects he referred to were the Round-headed Rampion growing on Cliffe Hill, the Adonis Blue butterfly and the Scarce Forester moth.

The term 'Lewes Downs' has subsequently been extended to cover all the hill country between Lewes and Mount Caburn, of which a significant proportion is now managed for its wildlife. Malling Down was purchased in the early 1980s by the Sussex Wildlife Trust, who were subsequently gifted Southerham Farm in 2001. Mount Caburn is a National Nature Reserve managed by Natural England. Collectively these extensive areas display nearly all the classic features of chalk downland.

Oxteddle Bottom, which runs north-west from Mount Caburn, is part of Natural England's National Nature Reserve on Lewes Downs. This classic stretch of 'naked' downland has not suffered as much as many areas from scrub invasion because it is relatively remote from major seed sources and continues to be grazed.

influence in persuading others to take action to protect wildlife, such as the local authorities which are empowered to create Local Nature Reserves. County and district councils have established twenty-two within the National Park. Hampshire County Council, for example, own and manage two special sites: Ashford Hangers National Nature Reserve and Shortheath Common Local Nature Reserve. However, in the midst of the current global financial crisis, some local authorities have been disposing of nature reserves where they can persuade wildlife charities to take them over.

Nature conservationists have been very active in the educational field, and television has also played a crucial role in making the general public more aware of not only the beauty and fascination of wild plants and animals, but also the many threats facing our natural inheritance. This publicity has done much to aid the growth of all the relevant charities, including national bodies such as the National Trust, RSPB, the Woodland Trust and Butterfly Conservation.

Post-war, the National Trust has once again taken a serious interest in nature conservation. It has played a crucial role in acquiring and managing large areas of the chalk downland, woodland and heathland in Sussex and Hampshire, including Black

Down, Woolbeding Common and important areas around Gilbert White's Selborne. A National Trust property of a different kind which is of note for its flora and fauna is the beautiful deer park of 283 hectares attached to Petworth House. Landscaped by Capability Brown, it features in several of J.M.W. Turner's paintings.

The RSPB has made a most valuable contribution to nature conservation by establishing a large reserve and a popular visitor centre at Pulborough Brooks in the Arun valley, where it has re-created wet meadows and heathland. A few miles south of Pulborough, the Wildfowl and Wetlands Trust has established its Arundel visitor centre, where it has also created a wide range of wetland habitats which harbour many wild creatures.

Despite all this effort by conservationists, some habitats have deteriorated and species have been lost. Those unfamiliar with nature conservation might wonder why this has happened when so many surviving sites are now managed by highly professional bodies. There have been the damaging historic factors already described and sometimes a lack of financial resources, but the simple truth is that our understanding of natural processes, species conservation and nature reserve management has been very slow to develop. The original concept was that all you had to do to a nature reserve was to put a fence around it. Charles Rothschild himself said that *'the only effective way of protecting nature is to interfere as little as possible'*. Even in 1950 Cyril Diver, the first Director General of the

British White cattle on Stedham Common Nature Reserve. This ancient breed is well suited to grazing heathland and overgrown pasture.

Nature Conservancy, was in favour of *'letting nature take its course'*.

It is only in the last fifty years that research has really begun to bear fruit and conservationists have gradually made progress in the management of reserves. Now it is understood more fully that there are few truly natural habitats in the UK and that most of our specialised plant and animal species are heavily dependent upon the intervention of man, for instance by coppicing, grazing domestic livestock or mowing. In recent times grazing has become a particularly important management tool. For example, the Sussex Wildlife Trust carries a stock of about 600 sheep and 70 cattle to graze and browse on its reserves and the Hampshire & Isle of Wight Trust, which has mainly relied on local farmers, is now building up its own stock of sheep and cattle.

Since their foundation just over fifty years ago, the Sussex Wildlife Trust and the Hampshire & Isle of Wight Wildlife Trust have now accrued a total of over 61,000 members, and have greatly expanded their public profile and political influence. Over the same period national voluntary bodies such as the RSPB have also benefited from a spectacular increase in public support. Rising donations and subscriptions from members as well as legacies are helping to finance a myriad of conservation initiatives, including land purchase and habitat restoration. Also heart warming has been the ability of the voluntary bodies to attract a growing army of unpaid volunteers, who are willing in their spare time to help clear scrub, repair paths, dredge ditches and otherwise restore degraded habitats. Volunteers also carry out vast amounts of biological recording. The financial savings accruing from many thousands of days per year of voluntary labour have enabled the two county Wildlife Trusts and other conservation bodies to punch 'far above their weight'.

An urgent task for the Nature Conservancy when it was founded in 1949 was to notify the local planning authorities of the key wildlife sites which it had designated as Sites of Special Scientific Interest (SSSIs). Unfortunately these SSSIs were initially given little statutory protection. In the drive to increase agricultural production landowners had been encouraged by the Ministry of Agriculture's 'ploughing grants' which took no account of environmental considerations. Several SSSIs were destroyed thanks to this indiscriminate agricultural policy. It was not until 1981 that SSSIs were given some legal protection, but even this was inadequate and it took further legislation in 2000 to ensure that they finally got the security they deserved.

In the meantime the Wildlife Trusts initiated a scheme to identify and protect noteworthy areas which were not given SSSI status. In Hampshire these are known as Sites of Importance for Nature Conservation (SINCs) and in Sussex as Sites of Nature Conservation Importance (SNCIs). They are now formally recognised by the planning authorities, which have an obligation to safeguard them from inappropriate development whenever possible.

At the other end of the scale, action is being taken at the international level that gives added status and protection to some of the most threatened species and most valuable sites. The EU Habitats Directive allows the designation of Special Areas of Conservation (SAC), the Birds Directive allows the designation of Special Protection Areas for birds and the Ramsar Convention allows the designation of wetlands of international importance. All of these have legal and policy-making repercussions for both national and local government.

On top of all the measures that have been taken to save individual sites, the whole of this special area of south-east England was given the strongest possible legal protection available in the UK when the South Downs National Park was confirmed in November 2009. The National Park Authority has a statutory duty to conserve and enhance the natural beauty and wildlife of the area, and all other public bodies operating within the National Park are now required to have regard to national park purposes. One of the great benefits is that the National Park Authority is in a position to bring together the statutory bodies, voluntary organisations, landowners and individuals to deliver a coherent strategy and programmes that will nurture and enrich the National Park.

Campaigning for a South Downs national park had begun in 1929 when the coast between Brighton and Eastbourne was threatened by development. Pressure for its protection continued over decades whenever the iconic landscape of the Downs was particularly threatened by developments or by the destruction of its wildlife habitats. In 1947 the Hobhouse Committee had recommended to the Government that the South Downs should be one of the twelve areas that should become national parks. However, in 1956 the National Parks Commission considered that national park status was no longer appropriate for the South Downs as the opportunities for open-air recreation had been undermined by ever-increasing cultivation. Fortunately, this unconvincing argument did not prevail. In the end the creation of the National Park was the culmination of a crusade driven by the South Downs Campaign. Founded in 1990 by the Council for National Parks, CPRE, the Ramblers Association and the Sussex Wildlife Trust, this unprecedented campaign grew to have a membership of some 160 national, regional and local environmental organisations, community groups and parish councils.

Within the National Park there are currently 86 SSSIs covering 9,945 hectares, including the 9 National Nature Reserves, which total 840 hectares. At the international scale 13 SACS have been designated as well as one RAMSAR site (the Arun valley); parts of these also have SSSI status. At the local scale 853 SINCs and SNCIs account for 14,219 hectares.

Amongst the many volunteers who do conservation work, these two from the Territorial Army are helping to clear unwanted Rhododendron. This non-native shrub can look magnificent when in flower, but it is highly invasive and left to itself quickly forms impenetrable thickets that shade out native plants.

The wider countryside

Whilst nature reserves are hugely valuable in the quest to protect and conserve nature, they are inadequate on their own. They are often isolated islands surrounded by alien landscapes and they occupy only a small proportion of the land. Because of their relatively small size they are very vulnerable. A single disaster, such as wildfire, can wipe out all the individuals of a particular species, and there is less room for species to escape from competition. Increasingly, conservationists are focusing on wildlife in the wider countryside and are attempting to create wildlife corridors that link areas together at a so-called 'landscape level'. Government agencies, conservationists and co-operative landowners are all playing crucial roles in stemming the loss of species and habitats and in restoring neglected areas across the whole countryside.

In the late 1970s, there was a growing realisation of the adverse environmental consequences of the current farming policies. Various agri-environment incentive schemes were then developed by successive UK governments in conjunction with the European Union to persuade landowners and farmers to act to conserve and enhance wildlife. The chalklands of the South Downs were one of the first five areas to be designated under the Environmentally Sensitive Areas scheme established in 1986. Special funding was made available to farmers that aimed to halt the loss of key wildlife habitats, to protect archaeological sites and to enhance the landscape. It was an important step forward and the visual appearance of the chalk hills was improved because large areas of arable were reverted to grass.

Paradoxically, it was the over-production of farm crops in the 1980s that led to a further respite for wildlife, particularly birds. In order to reduce the huge surpluses which had created 'food mountains', the Set-aside scheme was introduced in 1988, initially as a voluntary measure, but then as an obligation for farmers to reduce their productivity by setting aside a proportion of their cropped farmland. The resulting fallow fields yielded colourful arrays of wild flowers, seeds for birds and quiet areas for ground-nesting species. The Set-aside scheme was abolished in 2008, following two seasons with poor grain yields. Although not intended as an environmental measure, the wildlife benefits of this scheme were significant and the voluntary Campaign for the Farmed Environment was introduced in 2009 in order to try and retain those benefits.

The 1991 Countryside Stewardship Scheme and its successor the Environmental Stewardship scheme launched in 2005 have both made significant contributions to the conservation of wildlife and the enhancement of landscape quality and character. These crucial agri-environment schemes are negotiated through the Europe-wide Common Agricultural Policy, which means that vital decisions determining the future of our countryside are not entirely in the hands of the United Kingdom.

A public initiative with a very positive outcome was led by the South Downs Joint Committee (predecessor of the South Downs National Park Authority) which raised £1.2 million for the Sussex Wealden Greensand Heathland Project. This scheme has done much to restore many neglected heathlands and has usefully increased the area of open heath habitat in the South Downs National Park.

The Sussex Wildlife Trust's West Weald Landscape Project promotes integrated management of the landscape in the West Weald, including improved conservation of four core forest areas and improved wildlife connections and land management across the whole landscape, which encompasses 240 square kilometres. The Trust's Sussex Wetland and Rivers Partnership promotes the sustainable management of Sussex rivers and their landscapes and the restoration of wetland habitats, including the creation of more sustainable wetland ecosystems. The project is working with natural processes to recover the endangered Otter, Water Vole and Black Poplar tree. The Wildlife Trust in Hampshire is actively involved in a project to save our native White-clawed Crayfish from extinction.

The Government recognised the importance of landscape scale projects by launching a radical new initiative in 2012 for initially twelve 'Nature Improvement Areas for England'. The South Downs National Park Authority got off to a flying start by being chosen to manage one of the areas. It was awarded £608,000 in support of a project named 'The South Downs Way Ahead'.

This focused on protecting and enhancing South Downs chalk downland, which is not only vital to the survival of rare and endangered wildlife but is relied on by millions of people to provide clean drinking water and valuable green space for recreation. The project is made up of 28 partners including farmers, conservationists, Non Government Organisations (NGOs), community groups, government bodies, research organisations and water companies, as well as the National Park Authority. Amongst the objects is a scheme to broaden the South Downs Way National Trail as a semi-natural corridor and to re-create species-rich chalk grassland.

Despite the many dramatic changes to the countryside since Gilbert White's days in the 18th Century, often at the expense of wildlife, one must not be too pessimistic. There are some areas that have altered little and we can be thankful that the very special qualities of the South Downs that still exist have been formally acknowledged and much is being done to nurture and enhance this magical part of England. We will now look more closely at this rich diversity of habitats.

The view westward across the tree-clad Weald from the sandstone ridge of Older Hill on the National Trust's Woolbeding Common.

Woodlands occupy 24% of the area of the South Downs National Park and are of considerable interest to naturalists. The greatest concentration is in the western Weald, which is one of the most wooded areas in England and Wales. The origin and antiquity of the woods is of crucial importance when assessing their value for nature conservation.

Woodlands

Primaeval forests

During the last century a great deal of research was done on the history of forests and woodland in Britain. Much information was revealed through the analysis of tree pollen that has been preserved in peat beds for thousands of years.

When the climate gradually became warmer after the last Ice Age some 11,000 years ago, Birch and Pine woodland began to develop, similar in character to the woodland we see today in the colder climes of western Europe. As the climate got still warmer in the 'Boreal' period, Oak, Elm and Hazel gradually became dominant in the south. The succeeding warmer and wetter 'Atlantic' period saw an increase in Lime and Alder. A natural forest climax type consisting mostly of Lime and Oak came to dominate southern England, but it is now apparent that Hazel, Alder and Elm were also prominent and that the mix of species was determined by local soil and climatic conditions. These primaeval forests were not always dark, impenetrable places with a continuous tree canopy. Natural disturbance through storms, fire, erosion, flooding, as well as grazing and browsing by large mammals, would have created variety with some open areas resembling modern parkland.

The cultivation of land by Neolithic farmers began in a drier period at about the same time as a massive decline of the Elm began, perhaps linked to forest clearance by humans, but more probably the result of an early epidemic of Dutch Elm Disease. In the late Neolithic and Bronze Age Lime trees became less important components of the woodlands. It is thought they mainly grew on more fertile soils where the first farmers tended to settle. It was as farming began to gather momentum that Beech and Hornbeam arrived in Britain, but they did not become major forest trees until much later.

Woodland management

From the Iron Age onwards there were extensive clearances of trees by farmers, particularly on the drier, well-drained lands such as the chalk downland and the sandy heathlands. However, not all the primaeval forests were swept away. Some were recognised as being valuable assets and were managed, either as sources of timber and underwood, or as wood-pastures which yielded both wood products and grazing for animals. Many of these very old managed woodlands have survived, although their structures may have been modified over the course of time. They tend to be the ones that have the richest flora and fauna.

In the 1970s Neolithic and Bronze Age wooden trackways that date from about 4000 BC were discovered in the peat on the Somerset Levels. Their sophisticated construction, using many different sizes and shapes of wood from a variety of trees, suggests that these materials must have been harvested from woodlands that were coppiced. This remarkable discovery has proved that people were skilled in woodmanship from very early times.

In coppiced woodlands trees such as Oak were allowed to grow upwards into tall straight-stemmed 'standards' before being felled to provide hard-grained timber for constructing buildings, boats and other products. Forming an 'understorey' beneath the oaks were shrubs and smaller trees such as Hazel and Willow that were able to re-grow from their stumps or roots after being cut down or 'coppiced'. After some years the coppicing was repeated and the regrowth harvested to provide a regular supply of poles, fencing stakes, wattle or firewood.

Other areas of the former primaeval forest were used as wood-pastures, where cattle and deer grazed on the grasses and herbs and browsed on the trees and shrubs. Swine scavenged on the ground and were fattened on the autumn harvest of acorns or beech mast. Woodmen could not coppice in wood-pastures because the young regenerating growth would have been eaten by the browsing animals. They therefore harvested wood by 'pollarding'. Branches of suitable species of trees were cut off above the height that animals could browse and the main trunks, or 'bollings', were left to sprout new shoots from where the cuts had been made. This enabled the pollarded trees to produce successive crops of wood.

Evaluating today's woodlands

Scientists have undertaken detailed studies of the trees, shrubs and flora of existing woodlands and have linked this information to historical evidence. Using the earliest reliable maps, from around AD 1600, as a base line, they have categorised woodlands as either 'ancient' or 'recent'.

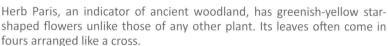

Herb Paris, an indicator of ancient woodland, has greenish-yellow star-shaped flowers unlike those of any other plant. Its leaves often come in fours arranged like a cross.

Another important distinction has been made: woods that have been cleared and then re-planted much later, or established as new plantations on ground that has not been used continuously as woodland, are defined as 'secondary' woodlands. The biodiversity of these secondary woodlands tends to be less rich than that of ancient woods.

Some plants, such as Herb Paris, Bird's-nest Orchid and Butcher's Broom, are restricted to ancient woodlands and are known to be very slow colonisers of plantations or secondary woodlands. Dr. Francis Rose, with the support of Richard Hornby, drew up a list of Ancient Woodland Vascular Plants which he regarded as the most reliable indicators of ancient, botanically-rich woodlands in

the different regions of England. His analysis demonstrated the exceptional quality of some of the ancient woodlands within the designated South Downs National Park. Of the sixty-three richest sites in Hampshire, Sussex, Kent, Oxfordshire and Berkshire, the Upper Greensand Hangers, the Wealden Edge Hangers and Ebernoe Common occupy three of the top four places.

Hampshire Hangers

Selborne lies in the heart of the East Hampshire Hangers, a most striking area of high scenic value dominated by dramatic steep 'hanger' woodlands and gentler summit areas on both the Chalk and Upper Greensand at the eastern edge of the Hampshire Downs. The area includes, according to Francis Rose, some of the ecologically most interesting and diverse series of chalk woodlands in the British Isles. Over 571 hectares have been scheduled as of international importance for the presence of Lime-Maple forest, Beech forest and, at Noar Hill, chalk grasslands. The woods include areas with old pollards on former wood-pasture as well as high forest. The biodiversity of the whole of the Hampshire Hangers is incredibly rich. The flora has many rare or locally distributed species including the native Mezereon, Columbine, Red, White, Violet and Green-flowered Helleborine, Narrow-leaved Helleborine and Bird's-nest Orchid. Here ferns such as Hart's-tongue, Soft Shield-fern and Lady-fern are plentiful. The largest concentration of Italian Lords-and-ladies in Britain occurs on the damper areas along the scarp foot, often growing amongst chalk rubble. The Hangers are also one of the finest sites for mosses and lichens in Britain.

The zigzag path constructed by Gilbert White and his brother provides access up the steep Beechwood hanger to Selborne Common. The highest point has an elevation of 207 metres. The soil is developed on clay-with-flints, overlying the chalk. Cattle now graze the old flower-rich wood-pasture and the ancient practice of pollarding trees has been re-introduced. Selborne Common, with its suitably damp and calcareous environment, is a nationally important site for molluscs, having at least 41 species. Selborne Hanger is a haunt of the rare Mountain Bulin, a mainly central European snail with very scattered outposts across southern England, mostly in old woods. Elsewhere in the National Park it occurs very sparingly in two places on the South Downs.

Ashford Hangers National Nature Reserve.

© Charles Cuthbert

The elegant Violet Helleborine is an uncommon orchid found in shady woods.

Unusual in having no chlorophyll, the Bird's-nest Orchid is most often found growing in deep shade under Beech.

White Helleborine is another woodland orchid, often associated with Beech.

The wooded north-facing scarp slope of the South Downs at Poynings.

West Sussex wooded escarpments

The ancient hanger woodlands on the steep scarp slopes of the western South Downs stretch almost unbroken from the River Arun to the East Hampshire Hangers. The hanger woodlands between Bignor and Duncton and further west at Rook Clift are of such great interest that they have been granted international recognition. They are particularly notable because of the presence of one of Britain's rarest native trees, the Large-leaved Lime.

Both Small-leaved Lime and Large-leaved Lime were components of the woodlands in south-east England from 7,000 to 7,500 years ago onwards and pollen of lime, possibly the Large-leaved species, has been recorded in peat deposits in the Arun and Ouse valleys. Although widely planted in parks and gardens, the native population of Large-leaved Lime was long believed to be limited to just a few areas in the South Pennines, north-east Yorkshire and near the Wye valley, where it is confined to limestone slopes. Its presence in the South Downs hanger woodlands was only discovered in 1987 and it is now acknowledged that these particular trees are truly native. Almost all the Large-leaved Lime sites in the South Downs National Park are in ancient coppiced woodlands and exist as coppice stools, some of which are very large and of a great age.

At one site in particular – Rook Clift in West Sussex – a good population of the Large-leaved Lime exists in intimate mixture with Wych Elm, Field Maple, Whitebeam and Hazel, perhaps giving an impression of what woods on chalk scarp slopes looked like in pre-Neolithic times. No similar woods are known in other chalk regions of Britain.

The West Sussex escarpment woodlands have a high proportion of ancient woodland indicator plants and also a rich mollusc fauna, including the rare Cheese Snail, which mostly lives in leaf litter and under fallen timber. Fly Honeysuckle, which frequents woodland edges and scrub, is believed to be native in England only in this part of the South Downs and at Wilmington in East Sussex.

© Tony Mundell

Although Lime trees are often planted in parks and gardens in Hampshire and Sussex, the extremely rare native, the Large-leaved Lime, grows naturally in a few woods on the South Downs escarpment.

Kingley Vale National Nature Reserve in West Sussex, looking across to the famous Yew wood.

Yew woodlands

The Yew is a widely planted tree in Britain, closely associated with churchyards and renowned for growing to a great age. It was the preferred source of wood for the long bow. The wild woods where Yew is the dominant tree would seem to be mainly confined to shallow dry soils on chalk and limestone in the south and west. Pure Yew woods are relatively rare in Europe and in the south of England they tend to occur in patches where old Beech trees have fallen, for example on unstable slopes.

There are quite large stands of Yew woodland in some sheltered chalk valleys at Butser Hill, but Kingley Vale National Nature Reserve, near Chichester, is dominated by its magnificent ancient Yew wood, which is recognised as one of the finest of its kind in Europe. The steep slopes of the reserve are covered in a dense canopy of Yew trees, including weirdly shaped giants with gnarled branches and often multiple trunks. Views differ regarding the age of these trees, some suggesting that the oldest go back to pre-Christian times. The dense shade created by the evergreen Yew gives little opportunity for shrubs and a ground flora to develop. One of the few plant species that can survive under the canopy is Dog's Mercury.

The Yew is dioecious, which means that it has male and female flowers on separate trees. In the autumn the females produce masses of seeds, which are partly encased

Spider on a fruiting Yew tree.

© Sophie May Lewes

in fleshy scarlet arils. These provide a rich source of food that attracts large gatherings of birds of the thrush family: Blackbirds, Mistle Thrushes, Song Thrushes and large flocks of Fieldfares and Redwings feed voraciously during the winter. These birds provide prey for the resident Sparrowhawks and even Tawny Owls. Whereas the Yew seeds are eaten by birds and shrews they are highly poisonous to humans. The leaves are also very toxic to both animals and humans, particularly when ingested in large quantities.

An ancient Yew at Kingley Vale.

© James Giles/Wild Images, Natural England

Woodland on the chalk dip slope

The Downs in Sussex west of the Arun valley are much more wooded than those in the east. Here there are some superficial deposits of clay-with-flints resulting in a more clayey soil that is less calcareous and often more acidic. Oak and Hazel woodland tends to favour the deeper clay-with-flints while Ash and Beech grow on the thinner chalkier soils. Magnificent Beech woodlands grace many parts of the South Downs National Park. Gilbert White judged the Beech to be 'the most lovely of all forest trees, whether we consider its smooth rind or bark, its glossy foliage, or graceful pendulous boughs'. Beech trees arrived in Britain from the Continent, together with the Hornbeam, only about 7,500 years ago and long after oaks, elms and limes had become well established. Somehow Beech managed to spread widely, despite the competition provided by the many tree species that were already present. Yet Beech is not naturally an invasive species.

Beech trees cast such a dense shade that the ground flora is generally very sparse. Orchids are an exception to the rule and thrive in some places under Beech despite the low light conditions. Seedling Beech trees are often conspicuously absent. Many mature Beech woods on the Downs are remarkably even aged, which suggests that originally they were planted. After the 1987 Great Storm felled many venerable Beeches, seedlings in some places sprouted up to take their place, but as a general rule natural regeneration is very localised and fitful. There is a strong suspicion that Beech is not a true native on chalk, and that it has been planted on the Downs as an ornamental and for its valuable timber. Many suspect that Beech is a natural component of woodland only on sandy soils.

Where the chalk is only thinly and incompletely covered by clay-with-flints the ground flora can include many interesting species. Chappetts Copse, a Hampshire & Isle of Wight Wildlife Trust reserve, is a good example. This Beech woodland, though possibly of no great age, supports probably the largest Narrow-leaved Helleborine population in Britain along with good populations of Fly and Bird's-nest Orchids.

© Tony Mundell

Narrow-leaved Helleborine is a very local and declining species of orchid in Britain.

One of the special features of West Dean Woods is a magnificent stand of native Wild Daffodils.

Snowdrops, though now well-established in part of West Dean Woods, have probably escaped from a former cottage garden.

West Dean Woods are the best known West Sussex example of Pedunculate Oak woodland with Hazel coppice on the dip slope of the Upper Chalk. Documents indicate that the coppicing dates back to at least the sixteenth century, but it was allowed to lapse in the last century. The long continuity of woodland cover is demonstrated by the deep, undisturbed forest soils which overlie the Upper Chalk, and by the presence of some unusual mosses, liverworts and lichens, including a lichen *Lobaria scrobiculata* in its only known locality east of Devon. There is no public access to these woods without a permit, but they can be viewed from a public footpath on their western side.

The Sussex Wildlife Trust has had a lease of West Dean Woods from the West Dean Estate since 1975 and its first priority has been to restore the main area as a working coppice-with-standards woodland. This has been accomplished almost entirely by volunteers – a vast undertaking. The area was divided up into compartments and initially two were coppiced annually. Once a compartment has been coppiced and the ground opened up to light there is a spectacular change. Given the right conditions, the woodland floor becomes carpeted with spring flowers such as Celandines, Primroses, Bluebells, Wood Anemones, Violets, Bugle and Wood Spurge. This colourful display is at its peak from two to four years after coppicing and then dwindles as the growth from the stools takes the light away from the ground once again.

The secretive Hawfinch is present in this area, as is the Dormouse, which thrives in the coppiced woodland and is a welcome resident, but the re-introduction of coppicing was too late to prevent the demise of the Pearl-bordered Fritillary. The precise ecological requirements of this butterfly are now much better understood. Its caterpillars feed on violets, preferably young seedlings that have grown on warm ground that has recently been made bare. It is hoped to reintroduce the Pearl-bordered to West Dean Woods when management modifications have created wider rides and other areas where violets can flourish. The only healthy population of this most attractive butterfly in West Sussex is at Rewell Wood, a large ancient woodland complex with extensive areas of Sweet Chestnut which is actively coppiced. It has conifer and beech plantations and chalk grassland with wide rides that support a rich flora and fauna. The rich but-

In the mornings male Purple Emperors come down to the ground to feed on putrid flesh or dung, or to drink from puddles, and this less than regal behaviour provides the best opportunity for seeing them.

terfly fauna includes Dingy Skipper, Grizzled Skipper, Green Hairstreak, Duke of Burgundy, White Admiral and Purple Emperor.

The Purple Emperor is one of Britain's largest and most beautiful butterflies and its national stronghold in the South includes a number of woods in the National Park. For centuries it was the ultimate prize for collectors. The literature is full of colourful descriptions of the chase and the first netting of a specimen. In a book devoted entirely to this species, 'Notes and Views of the Purple Emperor', Ian Heslop quoted his statement made in 1953: 'I have caught exactly as many Purple Emperors as I have shot Elephants, viz. four in each case: but I think I would rather have one of the former as I would all four of the latter.' Fortunately today's lepidopterists derive their greatest pleasures in an even more challenging task – shooting this fantastic butterfly with a camera.

Naturalists' fascination with the Purple Emperor lies in its elusiveness as well as its undoubted rarity. Even in its best-known colonies, such as one in Alice Holt Forest, the adults may not be seen because they spend most of their time flying above the trees and feeding off aphid honey-dew that coats the leaves. The males are extremely territorial and will even see off birds if they fly too near their patches.

Another striking woodland butterfly is the White Admiral, a most elegant flier and glider, which also has one of its national strongholds in the National Park. The other notable woodland butterfly that one is likely to see is the Silver-washed Fritillary which flies in July and August. It is our largest Fritillary and a most attractive species. Sadly its numbers have declined but it is still to be found in some open areas of woodlands where there are violets to provide food for its caterpillars.

Little managed for over a century, the ancient woodland known as 'The Mens' is reverting to a near-natural high forest.

Ancient woodlands of the Low Weald

Of the many woods in the Low Weald categorised as ancient, two, 'The Mens' and Ebernoe Common, which are owned by the Sussex Wildlife Trust, are regarded as being of exceptional quality.

The Mens is a 159 hectare wood common to the north of Fittleworth. The higher Greensand areas are mostly beech-clad, but where the ground gradually drops down to the heavy, unyielding Weald Clay oak predominates. Some parts of The Mens have been woodland for at least one thousand years and probably since forest first developed in south-east England after the passing of the Ice Age. It is a remnant of the once dense forest 'Andredswald', described by the Venerable Bede in AD 731 as 'thick and impenetrable and the haunt of large herds of deer and swine'. In AD 953 it was a 'swine pasture' for people living on the coast at Felpham and a common with specific rights for the commoners.

From the 15th to the 17th Century it was an industrial centre, first for glassworks and then for ironworks. For glass-making, Beech provided fuel and its ash was used as a flux in the 'glasshouses'. During the iron-making period, The Mens continued to provide wood for fuel. A 1650 map shows that the area was still tree-clad, which suggests that it was never clear-felled and that trees were carefully conserved to provide a continuity of supply. A High Court ruling in the late 19th Century prevented the Lord of the Manor from creating enclosures to exclude commoners' grazing animals from areas where tree growth was to be encouraged, but then the commoners gradually ceased to graze their animals and the whole area was left almost untouched by humans.

From an ecologist's point of view this history has been of great importance because The Mens today is an extensive woodland that has been virtually unmanaged for over a hundred years, and it is reverting as close as one can get to natural processes without reintroducing Bison, Wolves and other long-vanished species. Fortunately, a plan to drive 400 kV electricity power cables through its centre was prevented following a Public Inquiry in 1963 and the Sussex Wildlife Trust purchased the whole woodland between 1970 and 1974. At that time it was the largest woodland owned by a conservation body in England.

Fungi are either parasites, which feed on living organisms, or saprophytes, which feed on dead remains. It is therefore not surprising that The Mens woodland, which has a variety of trees in different stages of growth and decay, is renowned for its fungal flora. Dead branches and trees, which would normally be cleared away from managed woodlands, are an important host for many species. As an example of the richness of the fungi in The Mens, over forty Russula species have been recorded in it, including three known from no other site in Britain.

Beeswax Bracket. This rare fungus most often grows on Beech and appears shiny as if it has been varnished.

Death Cap. This deadly poisonous fungus is mostly associated with deciduous woodland, especially Oak.

Coral Tooth. A rare species of conservation concern found on logs and stumps, especially Beech.

Magpie Ink Cap. An uncommon fungus usually found in Beech woods on alkaline soil.

Yellow Stagshorn. A common fungus found on conifer stumps and roots.

Porcelain fungus. This species often grows on the dead trunks and fallen branches of Beech trees.

North of The Mens and the adjoining Ide-hurst Copse is Ebernoe Common, another Sussex Wildlife Trust nature reserve. This oak and beech common is an ancient wood-pasture where grazing has now been re-introduced. By any standards Ebernoe Common is exceptionally rich in species. There is a diversity of forest structure, ranging from fairly open glades through to dense, old-growth forest. The site is recognised as internationally important due to the unusually high habitat diversity supporting a vital assemblage of threatened species. At least 375 species of vascular plants, including over 70 ancient woodland indicators, 114 species of mosses and liverwort, and 180 species of lichens and over 1,200 species of fungi have been recorded. The reserve supports a very rich and possibly unique community of bats. Fourteen of the seventeen British species have been identified, including Barbastelle, Bechstein's and Grey Long-eared Bats, which are found in very few other locations. Several of these species breed and roost in the woodland but forage over a wide area of surrounding countryside. They need an interconnected patchwork of woodland, well-wooded stream-sides, meadows and hedges. This is provided by the remarkably unspoilt Low Weald landscape adjoining Ebernoe.

Many kinds of beetles are dependent upon dead and decaying wood and these ancient woods contain an unusually high number of species including some national rarities.

Barbastelle Bat, one of Britain's rarest species, forages for moths in mature deciduous woodland and surrounding areas of open country.

An even rarer species found in old-growth woodland is Bechstein's Bat.

© Hugh Clark/Sussex Wildlife Trust

Ischnomera sanguinicollis superficially resembles a soldier beetle. Nationally scarce, it can be found extracting nectar from the flowers of trees and shrubs in ancient woodland and wood pasture.

Stenurella nigra is a small, black and very scarce longhorn beetle that can be seen nectaring on flowers close to woodland in spring and early summer.

Platystomos albinus is a nationally scarce weevil that resembles a bird dropping. The larvae develop in dead and decaying wood. It is also associated with the fungus *Daldinia*.

Hornet Beetle is a large and impressive longhorn beetle that mimics a hornet or a burnet moth. Very scarce, it is restricted to south-east England.

In 1900 the graceful Red Kite was confined as a breeding species in Britain to mid-Wales because of unremitting persecution by gamekeepers. Now Kites regularly patrol the skies over the South Downs National Park and have begun breeding again.

The Mens, Ebernoe Common and many other ancient woodlands on heavy clay are home to the Wild Service-tree or, as it was traditionally known, the Chequers Tree. Once highly esteemed by country-folk, this native species now languishes in comparative obscurity. A relative of the Rowan and Whitebeam, it has creamy flowers and maple-like leaves, which turn an impressive coppery red in autumn. South-east England is its national stronghold, although it does grow as far north as the Lake District. It spreads mostly by suckering and rarely produces seedlings, probably because its seeds only germinate after freezing solid for a period.

Wild Service-tree berries are hard and bitter at first, but if they are picked and stored they slowly ripen and become sweet-tasting. Cottagers used to store the berries for eating in the depths of winter. Inn keepers and farmers sometimes used the berries for flavouring drink, which may be why so many Chequers Inns exist, some with venerable Service-trees growing close by.

Ebernoe Common supports many breeding birds including Common Buzzard, Lesser Spotted Woodpecker, Nuthatch and Treecreeper. The Common Buzzard was once confined to the West Country because of persecution by gamekeepers and pesticide poisoning, but in recent years it has gradually extended its range eastwards, re-colonising former territory. It is not at all unusual now to see this large bird of prey flying overhead or to hear its distinctive call. It nests in many woodland habitats right across the National Park. The unmistakable Red Kite is also making a very welcome return to Hampshire and Sussex following a highly successful re-introduction of birds from Spain and Sweden that were initially released in Oxfordshire.

Ebernoe Common and the surrounding area have one of densest populations of Nightingales in Britain. They nest in dense scrub, preferably Blackthorn, and are associated with damper open feeding areas. Their singing is at its peak from dusk until dawn, but they can also be heard occasionally in the daytime between mid April and the end of May.

Deer have increased greatly in the National Park area in the last fifty years and have been causing significant damage to trees and shrubs in woodlands, although they also roam in the wider countryside. The Roe Deer is the commonest, and the only native species. The tiny Muntjac, which originally escaped from captivity, is also extending its range. There are groups of elegant Fallow Deer roaming wooded downland areas including Kingley Vale, but the finest herd in England is confined within Petworth Park.

Antlers lock in Petworth Park – the autumnal rut of the male Fallow Deer.

They are fascinating to see at any time, but one of the most spectacular wildlife events in the National Park has to be the Fallow Deer rut in October at Petworth, when all the deer gather together and there are fierce engagements between the rampant bucks and continuous roaring from competitors.

Many woodlands of nature conservation importance are now managed to reflect their historic past and to maintain their characteristic flora and fauna, but the Great Storm in 1987 was a stark reminder that even with careful management trees remain vulnerable. Vast swathes of woodlands were flattened in a few hours.

However, it was not a total disaster, for areas opened up to the sky were quickly filled with flowers and busy with insects. The tilted root plates provided habitats for ferns, fungi and mosses, and dead and damaged branches were exploited by nesting birds and wood-boring insects.

Chalk grassland plants, including Pyramidal Orchid, Common Bird's-foot Trefoil, Yellow Rattle and Yellow-wort, at Mount Caburn National Nature Reserve near Lewes.

Chalk Grasslands and Scrub

The semi-natural chalk grasslands of Sussex and Hampshire are amongst the finest in Europe. Their immediate visual appeal is matched by their obvious ecological value. The short springy turf is made up of an amazing variety of plants that crowd together in intimate association, all competing for root space in the shallow, often parched, calcareous soil. In summer the Downs are a carpet of colourful flowers that attract a legion of insects, especially bees, butterflies and grasshoppers. At some particularly favoured sites it is possible to find as many as 40 species of flowering plant in a square metre.

Before the arrival of the first farmers almost all the Downs would have been covered by forest, but there may well have been glades kept open by large grazing animals where chalk grassland species could establish themselves. As the farmers cleared more and more forest the chalk grassland species seized the opportunity to invade land set aside for pasture and spread across ever larger areas of downland.

Nearly all the chalk grassland plants and insects are intolerant of shading and quickly disappear if shrubs and trees invade the grassland. Constant cropping by sheep and rabbits is needed to prevent any invasion and encourage the growth of grasses and other low-growing plants that can withstand being chewed and munched. Paradoxical though it may seem, the biodiversity of the surviving chalk grassland also owes much to the relative infertility of the shallow chalk soils. Soil poverty promotes species richness. Some of these chalkland specialists have very deep roots, whilst others have waxy or hairy leaves to avoid desiccation on the warm, open ground.

During the 15th and 16th Centuries the rising price of wool meant that less and less downland was cultivated. Large areas of former arable were converted to pasture, and the Downs became a vast open 'sheep-walk', remnants of which survive as the species-rich chalk grasslands of today.

Unfortunately the ecological interest of grasslands is greatly reduced when artificial fertilisers are applied. The ranker and more vigorous grasses put on a spurt of growth (as do the Cowslips, which is perhaps surprising) and the sheep benefit from having more to eat, but unfortunately the more delicate and slow-growing plant species are crowded out and disappear.

Sadly only about 5,608 hectares of the species-rich ancient chalk grasslands remain in the National Park, about 4% of the total area of the Downs. Now that the value of these very special habitats is more widely appreciated, every possible effort is being made to protect existing areas and to expand them. It only takes a few years for newly created grasslands to become colourful and busy with insects, but it took hundreds of years for the ancient herb-rich grasslands to evolve. Re-creating their special characteristics will be a difficult and challenging task.

Clustered Bellflower and Marjoram flower in late summer on the Downs.

Traditional grazed chalk grasslands

Such is the variety of plants that make up old chalk grassland that it is impractical to name more than a small selection. Amongst the grasses, Sheep's Fescue is often dominant, but is speedily suppressed when coarser species are allowed to grow up unchecked by grazing animals. Members of the vetch family are much in evidence, especially the golden-flowered Horseshoe Vetch and Common Bird's-foot Trefoil. Adding innumerable touches of blue and mauve to the scene are Small Scabious, Common Milkwort and Round-headed Rampion. Clus-tered Bellflower, one of the treasures of the downland, has bell-shaped flowers of a rich purplish-blue. The Gentian family is represented by three contrasting species: Autumn Gentian or Felwort, which has small purple flowers, Common Centaury with delightful pink flowers, and aptly named Yellow-wort. Mention must also be made of Wild Carrot with its impressive umbels of white flowers (frequently with a single central floret that is dark red) and two other large white flowered perennials: Dropwort and Oxeye Daisy. Yellowish-flowered Wild Mignonette and Weld are often to be found where the ground has been disturbed. Easily overlooked because of their small size are three tiny white-flowered plants: Eyebright, Fairy Flax and Bastard Toadflax. Diminutive Squinancywort with its tiny pink and white flowers was once believed incorrectly to provide a cure for sore throats (or quinsy).

For many visitors to the Downs the most memorable plants are members of the orchid family. The more ubiquitous species such as Fragrant, Pyramidal and Common Spotted Orchids can be present in large numbers; other species such as the tiny Burnt-tip Orchid and Musk Orchid are very local.

Fragrant Orchids on Malling Down near Lewes.

Burnt-tip Orchid. This dainty and easily overlooked species has become much scarcer on the Downs in recent years.

Common Spotted Orchid grows in huge numbers on the South Downs, particularly on north-facing slopes and in old chalk pits.

© Malcolm Emery/Natural England

© Victoria Hume/Sussex Wildlife Trust

Chalk grassland harbours many herbs with aromatic leaves that scent the air. Kipling in his much loved poem 'Sussex' compared the all-pervading fragrance of Wild Thyme on the Downs to the scent of 'dawn in Paradise'. Marjoram is locally plentiful on the Downs and is another sweet-smelling member of the Labiate family. Further aro-matherapy is provided by Lady's Bedstraw, which has yellow flowers that smell strongly of honey.

Some of the oldest and finest chalk grass-land survives on slopes that are too steep ever to have been ploughed, particularly on the more precipitous parts of the chalk escarpment. Gradients on the dip slope are generally gentler, and where chalk grassland is found it is usually of relatively recent origin, replacing areas of arable that were cropped in the not too distant past. The flora and fauna reflect the varying age of the grassland. Areas that have not been ploughed since the Napoleonic wars have richer assemblages

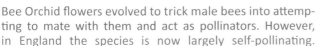

Bee Orchid flowers evolved to trick male bees into attempting to mate with them and act as pollinators. However, in England the species is now largely self-pollinating.

Early Spider Orchid, despite its name, is pollinated by sexually confused bees. In the National Park it is found regularly at only a few sites in East Sussex.

of plants and animals than more recently created grassland. That elegant relative of common Ragwort, Field Fleawort, is found only in places such as Iron Age earthworks that appear not to have been ploughed for at least 3000 years, if at all. It is evidently an extremely slow colonist of chalk grassland. As a general rule, Common Rock-rose occurs only in grassland that is several centuries old. Dropwort, Squinancywort, Common Milkwort and Bastard Toadflax are also restricted to old grassland. Many orchids, by contrast, are speedy colonists, appearing on quarry spoil tips and on the sides of new road cuttings after only a few years.

Chalk grassland on south-facing slopes is more sun-baked and prone to drought than grassland on cooler north-facing slopes, and as a result harbours many species that have predominantly southern and central European distributions. The sunny, south-facing slopes of Castle Hill National Nature Reserve east of Brighton for example are particularly rich in species. The star attraction is the diminutive but attractive Early Spider Orchid, which reaches its northern limit in southern England, Belgium, the Netherlands and central Germany. As an early flowerer, the orchid is intolerant of grazing in spring or early summer. Bastard Toadflax is another warmth-loving plant species at Castle Hill that reaches its northern limits in southern England. It favours very short, sunny turf and is a hemiparasite, attaching itself to the roots of other plants.

Musk Orchids have tiny, sweetly-scented flowers that attract a variety of insect pollinators. They have suffered a drastic decline in recent decades because of summer droughts and insufficient grazing.

Numerous species of snail inhabit the dry chalk grasslands of the National Park. Some are relatively recent immigrants, for example the Carthusian or Chartreuse Snail, which seems to have been accidentally introduced by Neolithic farmers. The South Downs are one of its few British strongholds. Other species, such as the Ribbed Grass Snail and the oddly named Moss Chrysalis Snail, were widespread on the Downs at the end of the last Ice Age when the area was treeless tundra. Somehow they survived the spread of forests and were able to expand their populations again when farmers started to cut the trees down. Both species are common in short chalk grassland. Much rarer is another tundra relic, the so-called Heath Snail, which thrives on only the most sun-baked and heavily grazed chalk slopes.

Although many downland plants thrive on sun-drenched sites, others shun them. Musk Orchid, for example, is very shallow-rooted and suffers greatly during prolonged droughts. It is mainly a plant of cool damp north-facing slopes, but even here it is vulnerable. It used to grow in great numbers on north-facing slopes at Malling Down Nature Reserve at Lewes, but the great drought of 1976 almost totally eliminated it, and even now its numbers show no signs of recovering. It has fared rather better in West Sussex, for example at Kithurst Hill near Storrington, and it continues to thrive at the Hampshire & Isle of Wight Trust's reserve at Noar Hill near Selborne.

Some chalk grassland butterflies are very exacting in their ecological requirements, none more so than the celebrated Adonis Blue. Its caterpillars live solely on Horseshoe Vetch, and the species is restricted to south-facing slopes where the vetch is well established. The female butterflies are very choosy about where they will lay their eggs, and invariably select vetch plants less than 5 cm high that have been closely cropped by sheep or rabbits. The reason seems to be that the warm microclimate associated with the low-growing plants aids the caterpillar's development, and also benefits the red and black ants that guard it.

The Adonis Blue has more colonies on the chalk in the eastern part of the South Downs National Park than in the west, perhaps because the climate in the east is slightly warmer and drier. The closely related Chalkhill Blue has caterpillars that also feed on Horseshoe Vetch, but it is a much more widespread downland butterfly and in favourable years vast numbers can be seen in late summer on Old Winchester Hill, for example.

Sharing the same habitats as the Adonis and Chalkhill Blues are the distinctive day-flying moths of the Zygaenidae family. The Six-spot Burnet and the scarcer Five-spot Burnets are unmistakable with their velvety-black wings that have prominent red spots. Their caterpillars feed on Common Bird's-foot Trefoil. The iridescent-green Forester is locally fairly common on the eastern chalk downs. The even more localised Cistus Forester, whose caterpillars feed on Common Rock-rose, frequents the Devil's Dyke and the Lewes Downs. Unfortunately the Scarce Forester, which was one of the species that led to the Lewes Downs being placed on Charles Rothschild's list, has now become so rare that it is in danger of extinction on the South Downs.

Chalkhill Blues feeding on Fox dung.

A Six-spot Burnet moth on a Knapweed.

A Scarce Forester photographed on the South Downs.

Duke of Burgundy, showing the characteristic two rows of white spots on the underwing that distinguish it from a Fritillary.

Dark Green Fritillary, one of the largest Downland butterflies.

The fascinating Duke of Burgundy butterfly was once categorised as a Fritillary, but is now known to be the only European representative of an exotic Neotropical family, the Metalmark. It has suffered a dramatic national decline, but thanks to the research work of scientists, who have identified its exacting habitat requirements, and the dedicated volunteer members of

Butterfly Conservation, who have been actively managing its few remaining locations, its population is more secure in some of its remaining colonies. Most of the sites in the National Park are on the chalk. Unfortunately the species is very sedentary and so it remains in isolated colonies with little prospect of dispersing to new territories.

One of the preferred habitats of the spectacular Dark Green Fritillary butterfly in the south of England is flower-rich open chalk downland. Although it is much less common than formerly, there are still a few colonies on the South Downs where the Hairy Violet, its caterpillar's foodplant, grows. It is on the wing in mid-summer and is a strong flyer, able to cope with windy conditions, but its territory is not very large.

There is a well-known colony of Duke of Burgundy at Noar Hill. The Duke's caterpillars feed on either Cowslips or Primroses, but the female is incredibly fussy and only chooses to lay her eggs on plants in their prime in half shade that have large glossy leaves.

© Roger Wilmshurst

Northern Wheatear, a common spring and autumn migrant that no longer breeds in the National Park.

Chalk scrub

Preventing scrub from invading species-rich chalk grassland is a necessary but difficult task. Experiment is often needed to decide precisely what levels of grazing are appropriate at a particular site. The traditional stocking rate of one sheep per acre per year can be too much in one area and too little in another. In the interwar period some areas of downland became quickly scrubbed up despite being regularly grazed by sheep, whilst others grazed only by rabbits remained clear of scrub. A lot depends on whether the grassland in question is located near existing scrub or woodland, which can act as a seed source. In Sussex a discontinuous belt of trees and shrubs roughly follows the base of the chalk escarpment, separating the chalk grassland above from the arable fields and pastures of the Weald below. All the evidence suggests that this is a very old landscape feature. The chalk grassland on the scarp above this belt of trees and shrubs suffers greatly from scrub invasion because seed is always being dispersed into it.

Hawthorn is by far the commonest component of chalk scrub, and, once established, sometimes forms monotonously uniform stands. Birds disperse its berries far and wide, and young plants soon develop prickles to deter grazing animals. As the Hawthorns grow, they start to shade out the grassland, reducing its biodiversity. The bushes provide berries, perches and nesting places for birds but in other respects pure hawthorn scrub is only of limited interest ecologically.

The bird life of the Downs has seen many changes. Skylarks could formerly be relied upon to fill the skies with their songs, but have become scarcer in the last few years. Migrant Northern Wheatears used to nest on the Downs in large numbers in Victorian times, and shepherds in the past regularly trapped them for food. Since the Second World War Wheatears have nested only occasionally on the Downs although they are still a common passage migrant. It is a mystery why, in this more bird-friendly age, Wheatears have not recolonised the Downs.

The conservation of old chalk grassland might seem perfectly simple – apply sufficient grazing pressure and the plants and invertebrates will continue to thrive. Unfortunately, different species can have opposing grazing requirements. For example, Marbled Whites and some other downland butterfly species favour long grass, but Adonis Blue caterpillars, as already mentioned, require closely cropped sward. Attempting to reconcile the differing grazing requirements of different downland species can be a conservation manager's worst nightmare.

Elsewhere on the Downs, bushes of Dogwood, Purging Buckthorn, Blackthorn or Sloe, Dog Rose and Sweet Briar, Wayfaring-tree, Spindle and sometimes Hazel successfully compete with Hawthorn to produce scrub that is much more varied and botanically interesting. Even the ground flora can spring surprises. In sunlit gaps between the bushes Fly Orchids and Early Purple Orchids can sometimes be found. Another interesting and characteristic species of bushy places on the chalk is Ploughman's Spikenard.

Where rabbits congregate, Elder bushes are often found, and sometimes also Deadly Nightshade, with its sinister-looking purple flowers and poisonous berries. Both species deter seemingly even the hungriest rabbits. On open downland Common Rock-rose is another plant that is firmly shunned by rabbits.

Some scrub is dominated by Juniper. One of Britain's three native conifers, Juniper is an important food plant for many invertebrates. Strange to relate, it appears to be indifferent to soil pH and grows as well on dry sandy heathland in some parts of Britain as it does on the chalk. For some curious reason in the South Downs National Park and many other parts of England adult Junipers rarely produce seedlings. Indeed they often fail to produce berries with viable seeds. The sad fact is that the species is not regenerating fast enough to replace its visibly ageing populations, and some stands of old Juniper, for example at Levin Down in Sussex, are beginning to look decidedly moribund. Yet Juniper in the past was sometimes very successful at regenerating itself, as witness the fact

© Alexander Henderson/Sussex Wildlife Trust

Juniper berries are used in cooking and for flavouring gin.

that many stands of Juniper are even-aged. Research is underway to try to understand the dynamics of Juniper regeneration and save the species from oblivion, including a trial at Noar Hill being undertaken by Plantlife in conjunction with the Hampshire & Isle of Wight Wildlife Trust and Natural England. The trick may be to overgraze drastically for a few years to create bare soil into which the junipers can seed (closed sward prevents the seeds from gaining a foothold) then to undergraze for long enough to allow seedlings to become properly established.

Gorse thickets are commonly found on the South Downs, particularly on summits and upper slopes from which cold night air can drain off. Victorian and Edwardian landowners looked on Gorse with favour because it provided shelter for sheep in foul weather, cover for game such as Brown Hares, and a quick-burning fuel for their agricultural labourers and shepherds. The Gorse thickets were rejuvenated by periodic cutting and burning, but unfortunately this practice has largely fallen into disuse. As a result seedling trees have sprung up within the thickets, protected from sheep and cattle. In many places on the Downs modern Sycamore and Ash woods have replaced Gorse thickets that early in the last century were left unmanaged.

Traveller's Joy, or Wild Clematis, often colonises chalk scrub. In winter one's eye is caught by its mass of silvery fruits which give it its more appropriate name, 'Old Man's Beard'. This vigorous plant, which festoons hedgerows and trees along roadsides, provides a clear indication that one is on the chalk.

The reddish berries of the Wayfaring-tree are dispersed by birds.

There is much disagreement about how best to manage chalk scrub once it has developed. Everyone agrees that monotonous stands of Hawthorn need to be cleared, especially if patches of chalk grassland survive between the bushes, ready to grow back when the bushes are removed. But clearing dense Hawthorn scrub that has formed a closed canopy and shaded out all the original grassland just creates an unsightly area of bare ground, which can speedily become a tangle of brambles, nettles and other unwanted plants. Many years of strimming and grazing may be necessary to re-create the original grassland.

Some argue that botanically diverse scrub is best left alone, as an interesting habitat in its own right. The trouble is that the scrub, if unchecked, can spread into adjacent chalk grassland, and over time is liable to evolve into woodland, sometimes dominated by Sycamore, a non-native tree that sustains few native insects.

Ash trees pose a particular threat to undergrazed chalk grassland. Female trees can drop their seeds directly onto the turf, very quickly producing a grove of young trees with virtually no intervening scrub phase, as has happened, for example, in part of Ditchling Beacon Nature Reserve.

© Malcolm Emery/Natural England

Heather grows alongside chalk-tolerant plants at Lullington Heath.

Chalk heath

During the Ice Age wind-blown silt (loess) was deposited in some places on the Downs and later was churned by frost into the underlying chalk. The silt has given rise to small patches of acid soil, supporting lime-hating (calcifuge) plants such as Ling (Common Heather) and Bell Heather. Alongside these patches the bedrock lies close to the surface and normal chalk grassland has developed, dominated by the usual lime-tolerant (calcicole) species. This unexpected melange of species with opposed soil preferences growing cheek by jowl is known as chalk heath.

Chalk heath has become an increasingly rare habitat because many former sites have been either overrun by scrub or destroyed by ploughing, fertilising or liming. Chalk heath that has been ploughed can never be recreated. Ploughing makes the soil uniformly alkaline and no longer able to support the heathers and other acid-loving plants. Fertilising and liming chalk heath can also cause irreversible damage.

True chalk heath should not be confused with the normal heathland that sometimes develops where clay-with-flints, sands or gravels form cappings on the chalk. The vegetation of these cappings shows none of the intimate admixture of calcifuge and calcicole species that characterises true chalk heath.

Good examples of true chalk heath survive on the South Downs at Lullington Heath National Nature Reserve and at Belle Tout near Eastbourne, and in Hampshire at Butser Hill and Old Winchester Hill National Nature Reserve.

Chalk Heath and Grassland Management: The Case of Lullington Heath

Lullington Heath provides a classic example of the challenges facing all those managing chalk heath and grassland nature reserves. This reserve was heavily grazed by rabbits, but after Myxomatosis, the re-introduction of sheep grazing was not permitted by the water company because of concern over possible pollution of the water supply. This resulted in gorse scrub encroaching on the chalk heath and threatening its survival. So, in 1960, the Nature Conservancy cut rides through the gorse and began mowing trials in an attempt to retain or re-establish the chalk heath flora.

Further rides were cut in 1965 and 1968 and mowing has continued ever since. Mowing produces a rather uniform vegetation structure and so in 1975, New Forest ponies were introduced to browse scrub and to produce a more diverse grazed turf. Pony grazing has continued since that time, usually with three to four animals. The New Forest and subsequently Exmoor breeds have proved ideally suited to the task, thriving all year round on the available forage. The dense scrub has been opened up by their browsing and remaining isolated bushes are cleared by hand.

With the agreement of the water company, sheep have been reintroduced to the site, to graze both chalk grassland and chalk heath compartments. A hardy Welsh hill breed, the Beulah, was first used and continues to prove very successful on the chalk grassland. Hebridean sheep were subsequently introduced and they exhibited a stronger preference than Beulahs for browsing the woody shrubs and perennials. They are now used exclusively to maintain the chalk heath. The combination of sheep and ponies proved effective in maintaining short turf and in controlling most invasive woody perennials, but bramble still caused problems and in 1994 Bagot goats were introduced (1 billy and 5 nannies). By 2004, the herd increased in number to 30 animals. Although prone to jumping over fences and escaping, they proved very effective in controlling bramble and preventing further scrub encroachment because of their habit of ring-barking. They are exclusively browsing animals, while the ponies both graze and browse. The goats were deemed to have done all they could for the reserve, and were moved to another site in 2011.

A gradual, long-term programme of scrub clearance with grazing and browsing as follow-up can be a satisfactory method for reclaiming chalk grassland. Unfortunately, the same is not true for chalk heath that has succumbed to gorse invasion. Mature Gorse stands have a deep layer of fallen needles beneath them. The only way to re-establish the chalk heath is to scrape off this mulch, exposing the chalk and loess. Even though the soil pH has been altered by the Gorse needles, it is still possible to use seed harvested from areas of surviving chalk heath to return the habitat to a short turf. This approach has proved very successful at Lullington Heath. When the target for Gorse clearance has been reached, the site can then be maintained largely by livestock, with limited need for intervention with machines.

Summarised from a report by Malcolm Emery, Natural England.

© Robin Crane

Iping Common, one of the finest heaths in West Sussex.

Heathland

Casual visitors, seeing the magnificent heaths for the first time, will find them very different from other habitats in the South Downs National Park. They will encounter largely open landscapes mostly dominated by heathers, bracken, gorse bushes and trees that are either Silver or Downy Birches or Scots Pines. In winter these areas can appear very bleak, although they are lit up by the yellow flowers of Gorse, which blooms throughout the year. In summer the heaths are ablaze with carpets of flowering heathers and busy with many different kinds of birds, insects and reptiles. They are very popular with walkers, not least because the pathways are mostly on sandy soils that drain very quickly and remain passable throughout the year. The 1,544 hectares of heathlands within the National Park are found almost entirely on the outcrop of the Greensands.

History

In 1726 Defoe described the heathlands of southern England as 'sandy, wild and barren country'. Cobbett in 1822 was even more dismissive, describing Ashdown Forest with its fine heaths as 'verily the most villainously ugly spot I ever saw in England'. How attitudes have changed! It was not until after the First World War that heaths began to be valued both as a key wildlife habitat and as valuable open space, rather than mere 'waste'.

One might easily think that heaths are natural habitats, but this is far from the case. There is no doubt that the dwarf shrubs that grow on these acidic, nutrient-poor, sandy soils must have been grazed by wild animals in the past. However, the heathlands we have today are the product of centuries of active exploitation by man. Local people used them for grazing their cattle, sheep, horses and geese. They also cut gorse for feeding their domestic animals in winter and as fuel for their cottage fires, using it to create quick intense heat, especially for baking bread. Bracken was harvested for winter bedding for cattle. The trees and taller shrubs growing on the heaths were cut and gathered for firewood, and the turf and peat were periodically dug up to provide another source of fuel. Once active management ceases the heathlands rapidly become dominated by birch woodland, Bracken and coarse grasses. This leads to the gradual disappearance of the heathers and their associated fauna. If tree growth were left unchecked the heathlands would probably end up as climax oak and birch woodland, as has happened for example in parts of Shortheath Common in Hampshire. However, where pine trees have been introduced they rapidly take over.

Heather-dominated plant communities can be found on the mountains and moors of northern and western Britain, and superficially resemble lowland heath but differ in their plant and animal associates. Crowberry, for example, often grows alongside heather on cold, windswept upland moors, but is absent from the warmer, drier lowland heath of the south of England. Dwarf Gorse, by contrast, thrives only in the south. The differences are not just botanical. There are no Grouse to be shot on lowland heath, for example.

Lowland heath is confined to north-west Europe, mostly to areas of nutrient-poor sandy soils below 250 m (800 ft) but large areas have been lost because of management neglect or changing land use, such as afforestation, conversion to improved pasture or arable, and the building of new housing estates. The lowland heath of the South Downs National Park has also become seriously reduced in extent, and much more fragmented than it was formerly. It has been estimated that there were 7,500 hectares of heathland in West Sussex in 1813, but only 679 hectares in 1981, a reduction of over 90%. Fortunately, nearly all the remaining heathland areas in West Sussex now fall within the National Park and are being actively managed. Although there have also been significant losses of lowland heath in Hampshire, extensive areas have survived in the New Forest and at Woolmer Forest. Both these areas benefit from the added protection of falling within newly created national parks.

Woolmer Forest was one of Gilbert White's favourite haunts in Hampshire. In his day it was a deer forest. Today Woolmer Forest and Longmoor Inclosure are in a military training area covering in excess of 1200 hectares. The Hampshire & Isle of Wight Wildlife Trust signed a management agreement with the Ministry of Defence in 2006 which made provision for the Trust to

Woolmer Forest.

re-introduce grazing and other forms of conservation management to large areas of the estate. Woolmer Forest and Longmoor Inclosure are closely linked to the Thames Basin Heaths complex and so they form part of the largest and most diverse block of heathland in southern England outside the New Forest. Not far away is Shortheath Common, another notable Hampshire heath, renowned for its valley mire, quaking bog and fine stand of Cranberry.

The best West Sussex sites within the National Park include Lavington Common, the Heyshott-Ambersham Common complex and Trotton-Iping-Stedham Local Nature Reserve. However, these sites tend to be isolated from each other and there are still some extensive areas of neglected heathland between them that ought to be restored.

Heathland habitats

When one starts to look closely at heathlands it becomes apparent that there are several different habitats within them. Some can be identified by the presence of three different species of heather. Ling and Bell Heather, in conjunction with Dwarf Gorse, grow on what is described as Dry-heath. There is an intermediate damper stage known as Humid-heath, where there is more Cross-leaved Heath and less Bell Heather. Wet-heath is formed where the water table is higher and is typically dominated by Cross-leaved Heath and Purple Moor Grass. This grass grows in large tussocks and can completely carpet an area at the expense of other plant species. Where water is more or less permanently on the surface Valley Mires or Bogs have formed which provide perfect conditions for mosses, especially *Sphagnum* species.

© Robin Crane

Bell Heather and Ling.

© Susanne Frost/Hampshire County Council

Heathland bog with *Sphagnum* moss.

© Tony Mundell

Cross-leaved Heath.

Oblong-leaved Sundew with trapped damselfly.

Bog Asphodel flourishes on the wettest heaths in the National Park.

A most attractive plant that flourishes in some acid bogs is Bog Asphodel, a member of the lily family with spikes of brilliant orange-yellow flowers. Its rootstocks creep through bog-moss allowing the plants to spread over a wide area.

In Wet-heath it is well worth looking for the fascinating little Sundew plants. Oblong-leaved Sundew grows on bare, acid peat, often around the margins of the wetter areas. More rarely, it is also to be found growing in *Sphagnum* moss. Its more widespread relative, Round-leaved Sundew, shows a particular liking for *Sphagnum*. Both Sundews are carnivorous and survive in places where nutrients are in short supply by digesting insects which they trap on the sticky tentacle-like hairs that cover the upper surfaces of their leaves. Another specialist of acid bogs and wet heaths is Cranberry, which usually grows over *Sphagnum* moss. It has become much rarer through land drainage and the harvesting of

Sphagnum for the florist trade. Shortheath Bog has the largest remaining population of this attractive plant in the South of England.

Common Dodder is another plant that finds its resources in unusual ways. It is a parasite that grows on heathers, gorse and other species. Needing no chlorophyll, its leaves have become reduced to tiny scales. Its slender threadlike stems wrap themselves around the host plant and attach themselves with swollen suckers. The process continues until the Dodder has enveloped its host plant like a giant spider's web.

Like Sundews, the free-floating Bladderworts are plants that trap and digest animals. They have a special mechanism under water for trapping and digesting minute aquatic animals.

Cranberry in flower.

© Tony Mundell

Cranberry fruits.

© Tony Mundell

© Tony Mundell

Common Dodder, climbing on Ling and Gorse.

© Neil Fletcher/Sussex Wildlife Trust

Southern Bladderwort flowers irregularly and is easily overlooked when not in bloom.

© Tony Mundell   © Alan Price/Sussex Wildlife Trust

Two spectacular species associated with the Silver Birch, sharing brilliant red and white colours, are the Great Spotted Woodpecker, whose population has dramatically increased in recent years, and the highly poisonous Fly Agaric fungus that is only found with birch.

Heather communities go through distinct phases in their lives. In the pioneering stage the plants grow in open ground from seeds that may have lain dormant for up to forty years. As heathers grow slowly, open ground may remain between the plants for many years. Other vascular plants may colonise these openings, which are hot in summer and cold in winter. In the building stage the heather gradually excludes all other plant species. By the mature stage, from about twelve to twenty-eight years, mosses and liverworts develop on the soil surface since humidity beneath the closed canopy has increased considerably. In the degenerate phase the old heather become woodier and gaps develop as the plants die and other plants and heather seedlings begin to grow. As these phases change so the fauna changes. Some invertebrates are adapted to live amongst the young heather with the greater warmth and open spaces. Others favour the different conditions that develop as the structural changes in the heather take place.

Birch trees on heathlands are beautiful, but they can be a menace as they rapidly colonise bare ground between heathers and gradually shade them out until they are killed off. However, many birds forage amongst birch leaves for insects during spring and summer. The soft wood of older trees is ideal for woodpeckers and other birds to bore out their nest holes.

© Oliver Wilks/Sussex Wildlife Trust

© Paul Roberts/Sussex Wildlife Trust

Common Crossbill – its twisted beak makes it adept at prising open pine cones.

A brightly coloured male Dartford Warbler shows itself on a spray of Gorse.

The native conifer Scots Pine became extinct in southern England, due to commercial exploitation and grazing, about three to four hundred years ago. It was re-introduced into Sussex in the 18th Century and is another tree that now thrives naturally on heathland. The seeds in its cones are extracted by flocks of wintering Common Crossbills, using their powerful crossed beaks. A few pairs remain to nest early in the year and the number is increasing. Another species linked to conifers that has also been expanding its population is the once rare Pine Hawk Moth whose caterpillars feed on pine needles.

One of the worst threats to heathlands is *Rhododendron ponticum*, a shrub native of south-west Europe and around the southern Black Sea, which was introduced to this country in 1793 and has now become extensively naturalised. It is of the same family as our wild heathers (Ericaceae) and thrives on the same sandy and peaty soils. It has overwhelmed many areas, forming intractable thickets, and is very difficult to eradicate.

Heathland specialists

The best heathlands are notable for their breeding and wintering birds, including nationally important breeding populations of Dartford Warbler, Wood Lark and the European Nightjar. The elusive Hen Harriers have winter roosts in a few places.

Wood Lark. The National Park is a stronghold for this rare resident.

The Dartford Warbler is a continental species more closely associated with the Mediterranean, but it has colonised the southern heathlands of Britain. It has great difficulty in surviving our coldest winters and so its numbers vary greatly. It is confined to dry heaths where there is plenty of mature Gorse and is difficult to find except for singing males that perch on top of these shrubs.

The Wood Lark is another special bird closely associated with heathland in Britain. Its specific habitat is open ground with a few scattered trees and it is particularly attracted to areas that have been recently cleared. This species is unusually tame and can sometimes be seen at close quarters when it is foraging on heathland. The males start singing before winter has

departed and the pairs will start nesting very early. Some regard the Wood Lark's plaintive song to be as evocative as that of the Nightingale. It sings on the wing like other larks, but it also sings on trees and even on the ground.

European Nightjars.

If one wanders around heathland on a fine evening in late May, June or July, just after the sun has set, the presence of a European Nightjar may be confirmed by its extraordinary call – a continuous churring trill that can last for several minutes. One might also see this crepuscular bird hunting for moths or displaying to its mate. A most attractive species with long wings and tail, it glides with sudden twists and turns, like a gigantic moth. Sometimes it flies towards its human observers as if to inspect them.

Many heathland species of invertebrates have highly specialised lifestyles, which makes them very vulnerable to habitat changes. The Field Cricket is a classic example of a southern European species on the edge of its range in southern Britain. In the 18th Century Gilbert White described its behaviour in intimate detail and noted that it was frequent around Selborne though generally scarce elsewhere. He wrote that 'As their cheerful summer cry cannot but draw the attention of the naturalist, I have often gone down to study their mode of life'. He observed that 'they are shy and cautious and, feeling a person's footsteps, they stop short in the midst of their song and retire backwards nimbly into their burrows'.

By 1988 the Field Cricket had been reduced in the UK to just one site: Coates Common, a West Sussex heath. It is the subject of a Species Recovery Plan and has been successfully introduced to several other heathland sites in the National Park that now meet its exacting habitat requirements.

Heathland plants are adapted to live in habitats with low nitrogen levels and so they grow slowly. They are less vulnerable to herbivores than might be expected, and it is believed that they have developed defensive chemicals to dissuade invertebrates from feeding on them. There are therefore relatively few plant-eating species of invertebrate found on heathlands and those that do are species that can survive without high levels of nutrients. However, many carnivorous invertebrates occur that require sandy soil for burrowing or hot open spaces.

© Neil Hulme

Field Cricket entering its burrow.

Andrena fuscipes. A mining bee which collects pollen only from heather flowers.

Myopa fasciata. A fly which lays its eggs inside the abdomens of the mining bees *Andrena fuscipes*; then the larvae eat the bees from the inside outwards.

Nomada rufipes. A cuckoo bee which lays its eggs inside the nests of *Andrena fuscipes.*

Ampedus elongantulus. One of several colourful click beetles found on heathlands, the larvae of which develop in old trees.

Cryptocephalus biguttatus. A pot beetle, so called because the larva lives in a pot of its own dung, rather like Caddis fly larvae. This species is associated with low stands of Cross-leaved Heath in damp, mossy situations in full sun.

Cicindela sylvatica. A fearsome hunting Tiger Beetle which runs its prey down on hot, bare sand. The larvae ambush their prey from a hole in the ground on the edges of sandy tracks.

Ammophila pubescens. A solitary wasp which preys on the caterpillars of heather-feeding moths (this is of the Beautiful Yellow Underwing moth). The caterpillars are put, paralysed, into the wasp's burrow, where a wasp larva will feed on them.

Thyridanthrax fenestratus. This beefly aims its eggs into the nest burrows of *Ammophila pubescens.* Here they hatch and the fly larva waits until the wasp larva is fully grown and has pupated. Then it feeds on the wasp pupa.

The Silver-studded Blue is one of two kinds of butterfly particularly characteristic of heathland. Unfortunately its population declined dramatically in the 20th Century. Although generally scarce, these delicate little blue butterflies can be seen in large numbers in a few small colonies where the habitat is suitable. They are on the wing in June and July and are particularly sedentary, rarely moving more than 20–50 m over their lifetime, although a few individuals will disperse further to found or join new colonies. Like several blue butterflies of the same family, this species has a very close relationship with certain species of ant. The perfectly formed caterpillars of this butterfly stay in their eggs over winter but when they emerge in the spring they are immediately adopted by ants which take them back to their nests. The caterpillars come out to feed in the evening. The caterpillars pupate in or near the host ants' nests. After the adult butterflies emerge from the pupa they continue to be tended by ants until the moment when they make their maiden flights.

The Grayling is a butterfly associated with hot, dry places where the soil is poor and the vegetation sparse. Heathland has therefore been one of its typical habitats. Its decline in the last ten years is still puzzling experts and it has virtually disappeared from West Sussex. It has also suffered a dramatic decline on the South Downs chalklands. This interesting butterfly is renowned for its remarkable camouflage when resting on the ground. Its elaborate courtship behaviour is also fascinating and so it is hoped that attempts to re-introduce this species to its former haunts will be successful.

Freshly emerged Silver-studded Blue still tended by ants.

Amongst heathland moths of especial interest is one rejoicing in the name of True Lover's Knot, which feeds on heather. Huge numbers can be lured to moth traps when they are on the wing from June to August. The Beautiful Yellow Underwing is an attractive little moth whose larvae also feed on heather. Some of the moths that are referred to as heathland species are also found in other habitats, though they are more easily seen in the wide open spaces of heathland. The most spectacular of these species is the Emperor, which is our only representative of the silk-worm family. The males fly in daylight in April and May whilst the females fly at night. The scent (pheromones) emitted by the females is capable of attracting the males from very long distances. If one is fortunate one may find large green caterpillars of this species in August when they are seeking out suitable sites for forming their large silky cocoons amongst heather twigs. The Fox Moth flies at the same time as the Emperor. In some years large numbers of the big rich brown males may be seen flying about at high speed in the sunshine.

Emperor Moth and caterpillar.

Small Red Damselfly.

Downy Emerald Dragonfly.

When the autumn dews condense on their webs, one becomes aware of the huge number of spiders that live on heathlands. In a survey on Iping, Trotton and Stedham Commons 109 spider species were identified, including notable rarities and a species new to Britain.

Acidic bogs and wet heathland support the most diverse dragonfly and damselfly fauna in Britain. Many of the widely distributed species breed in the pools and lakes successfully because the water is too acidic for predatory fish to survive. Others specialise in these particular habitats and are restricted to them. The Small Red Damselfly lives in small unshaded bog pools and shallow mats of *Sphagnum* mosses. The nationally scarce Downy Emerald and the Keeled Skimmer also prefer acid peat conditions. The males of the Downy Emerald are most eye-catching with greenish-bronze abdomens and apple-green eyes. The nationally rare Club-tailed and the scarce Golden-ringed Dragonflies are found on Shortheath Common where 23 different dragonflies and damselfly species have been recorded.

Spiders' webs on a heathland Gorse bush.

The hot, dry soils of the better-drained heathlands are ideal habitats for reptiles and all six UK species are present in the National Park. Adders, Grass Snakes, Slow Worms and Common Lizards are quite common whilst the two rarest species, the Sand Lizard and the Smooth Snake, can be found on a few carefully managed sites.

Adders thrive on dry heaths. They are most likely to be seen in the spring, when they emerge from hibernation, or in autumn when they are seeking winter quarters. They bask in warm sunshine, often using the same spot every day, but if it is too hot they lie in the shade. It is very rare for humans to be bitten by them but local veterinary surgeons have to treat injured dogs quite often, particularly in the spring. Those wandering off the paths are most vulnerable.

Woolmer Forest is one of the few locations in Britain where the extremely rare and non-venomous Smooth Snake is present. Sand Lizards have suffered a serious decline but they have been successfully re-introduced to a few sites now that their habitat requirements are better understood. They need warm open heath with some shady areas so that they can move around and control their temperature. The females need soft bare sand in which to lay their eggs. The males are vivid green in the spring when they are courting the females. One is unlikely to see Sand Lizards, but there are large numbers of Common Lizards and if one walks through heather in the summer they are often seen scampering out of sight.

The Adder, Britain's only species of poisonous snake.

© Tony Mundell

Smooth Snake. This non-venomous species has darkish marks on the back but lacks the bold zigzag patterning that characterises the adder.

© Howard Inns/Amphibian & Reptile Conservation

Common Lizards often bask in the sun on rocks and tree stumps.

Male Sand Lizard. Unlike Common Lizards, which are vivaparous, Sand Lizards are oviparous. The eggs that they lay in underground burrows take many weeks to hatch.

The Natterjack Toad is identified by the pale yellow stripe down its back and by its attractive speckled colouration. Unlike the Common Toad, it cannot hop, but it can run and bury itself in sand very quickly.

Woolmer Forest is the only place in Britain where all twelve of our native reptiles and amphibians survive. Of the amphibians the most interesting and the rarest is the Natterjack Toad.

Management

The Natterjack Toad has been saved from extinction at Woolmer Forest by conservationists creating shallow pools and clearing its terrestrial habitat of birch and willow saplings. Other species of plants and animals dependent upon exacting habitat conditions also require a helping hand. There is a need for constant management on all existing heathland sites to maintain and enhance their biodiversity and recreational interests. The principal aim is to establish a mosaic of heathers at different stages of growth and to prevent the invasive spread of bracken, scrub and trees. There has been much experimentation in order to identify the best methods of accomplishing these aims. These include mechanical cutting, forage harvesting and chemical treatment of birch, pine, bracken and rhododendron. Turf with established heather is cut and sold to golf courses for heathland creation or restoration, leaving bare ground that is then colonised by fauna that thrive in the early stages of succession as new heather begins to grow from dormant seed. Increasingly, traditional grazing by domesticated animals is being re-introduced where it is practicable. Grazing prevents shrub and tree invasion and creates open spaces. A number of breeds of docile cattle are very effective, and moorland pony breeds like the Exmoor are also excellent for this purpose. It is vital that firebreaks are maintained to prevent catastrophic summer fires such as the one that burnt nearly all of Trotton and Iping Commons to a cinder in 1976. These uncontrolled fires are extremely destructive and all too often they are started by arsonists, or through thoughtless discarding of cigarettes. However, periodic controlled burning of heathland can be a useful management tool.

Heathland plant communities are adapted to soils with low levels of nitrogen availability. Unfortunately, emissions of not only carbon dioxide but also nitrogen oxides are steadily increasing as society becomes more industrialised. As a result, rates of nitrogen deposition on heathlands are also rising, increasing the availability and uptake rates of phosphorus. It is feared that these changes will have serious effects on heathland habitats and species abundances, particularly next to busy roads.

It is easy to take our rich heritage of heathlands for granted, believing mistakenly that they are well able to look after themselves. The reality is that if we are to retain and enhance them they will require constant annual expenditure and the dedicated care of wildlife conservationists.

Looking north from Harting Down.

The Wider Countryside

Farmlands

As described in the introduction, modern farming methods have had a very damaging effect on wildlife. Attempts are now being made with the latest agri-environment schemes to undo some of the damage. With the enthusiastic support of sympathetic landowners, notable improvements have been made within the National Park as well as elsewhere. Most sites of major wildlife interest are probably better managed now than ever before, but it is sadly the case that on many farms the plant and animals have suffered greatly.

The traditional practice of sowing cereals in the spring has increasingly been replaced by winter plantings. The consequence of this is that much more land is being ploughed soon after harvest and so there are far fewer winter stubbles that provide food for birds. This is one of the principal reasons for the dramatic reduction in many seed-eating species associated with farmland such as finches, larks, sparrows and buntings.

The distinctive 'Pee-wit' call and the rolling, tumbling display flight of the male Northern Lapwing was once one of the most frequent and evocative signs of spring in the countryside. These ground-nesting birds prefer to lay their eggs in a scrape amongst spring crops and then to take their fledglings to unimproved grazed meadows

© Darin Smith

Northern Lapwing. The declining numbers of this attractive grassland-nesting species are a cause of much conservation concern.

nearby, where worms, beetles and grasshoppers provide abundant food for them. Over 90% of the pairs in Britain traditionally bred on farmland and the recent domination of winter cereals and the decline in mixed farms with pastures for cattle and sheep have sadly led to a huge reduction in breeding Lapwings. One of the other major factors in the disappearance of these most attractive birds has been the large increase in the number of Foxes, now that there are far fewer gamekeepers to keep their population within bounds. These predators remorselessly hunt and kill young Lapwings before they can fly. At Amberley Wild Brooks and Pulborough Brooks, under the positive management of the Sussex Wildlife Trust and the RSPB, there are around 35 pairs nesting and in winter huge flocks of wintering Lapwings are welcome visitors.

© Richard Revels

Brown Hares boxing. Buck hares compete for does by kicking and biting each other, but the contests rarely end fatally.

The increase in Foxes has also been a significant factor in the reduction in the breeding success of Brown Hares, but even more important has been the loss of grasslands typical of mixed farms. Fortunately, these exceedingly nimble and unmistakable mammals with long black-tipped ears, prominent eyes and large hind legs are still to be found in some of the wide open spaces on the South Downs, especially where dog-walkers are excluded.

The largely nocturnal Stone Curlew is a bird that nests on open, bare, preferably stony ground or areas with vegetation height below 2 cm. Arable land needs to have short or sparse vegetation before being accepted, and is rarely suitable for nesting birds beyond May or June. In 1768 Gilbert White advised Thomas Pennant that in the breeding season 'I could shew you them almost any day; and any evening you may hear them round the village, for they make a clamour which may be heard a mile'. In 1938 Walpole-Bond wrote that there were 'quite sixty pairs of Stone-curlews breeding in Sussex'.

Changes in agricultural practices that destroyed most of the semi-permanent grasslands and the arrival of Myxomatosis, that left vegetation ungrazed by rabbits, were almost certainly the principal reasons why, after a steady decline in the 1960s and '70s, this fascinating bird ceased to breed in Sussex in the 1980s. Its return in 2007 and its continued breeding success in Sussex are thanks to the enthusiastic support of the landowners and the stewardship of dedicated ornithologists. It is only with the co-operation of farmers and landowners that this highly specialised bird will thrive.

The charismatic Barn Owl is much less common than fifty years ago. A farmland bird, it favours rough grassland where it can hunt voles and other small prey, but with agricultural intensification less and less of its preferred habitat remains. Finding insufficient food on farmland, hungry Barn Owls often resort to hunting along road verges and end up as traffic casualties.

Barn Owls also have difficulty finding good nest sites. Many old barns traditionally utilised for nesting have been converted into houses or replaced by unsuitable steel structures. In addition, many tall old trees with cavities large enough to accommodate Barn Owl nests have succumbed to storms and disease. With the cooperation of sympathetic landowners, conservationists are attempting to increase the numbers of breeding Barn Owls by erecting nest boxes on suitable trees and buildings as far away from major roads as possible.

Traditionally, the annual cutting of grass for hay in permanent meadows and pastures was followed by grazing by sheep and cattle. This system helped support an extremely rich array of wild flowers. In the post-war period most of these grasslands were treated with artificial fertilisers to increase yields and this encouraged the growth of coarse, fast-growing grasses and other species that overwhelmed and eradicated their companions. The more

Barn Owl.

© Darin Smith/Sussex Wildlife Trust

The reddish-purple flowers of Betony at Badlands Meadow.

frequent and earlier cutting of silage to feed animals living indoors was even more destructive of the floral diversity of the grasslands, and prevented ground-nesting birds from rearing their young. Today there are very few botanically interesting meadows remaining.

One splendid exception to the general rule is provided by the inappropriately named Badlands Meadow in the heart of The Mens woodland in West Sussex. This possibly mediaeval pasture boasts Adder's Tongue Fern, Betony, Dyers Greenweed, Lady's-mantle, Greater Butterfly Orchid and other treasures. Its remoteness and long history of 'light-touch' management has helped it maintain its astonishing bio-diversity.

Many once-common weed species of arable fields have now become extremely rare. Gone are the days when cornfields were often scarlet with Field Poppies or blue with Cornflowers. Even Corn Marigold has become scarce and Corncockle is on the brink of extinction, except as a garden plant. Modern methods of cleaning cereal seed have become so efficient that many weeds are now eliminated at source. The widespread application of herbicides destroys many weeds as they grow, and many farmers have switched to growing new cereal varieties that mature much more quickly than older varieties and can be harvested long before rival weeds can set seeds. The application of nitrogen fertilisers also benefits cereal crops more than the associated weeds, which get crowded out.

Britain's best-known arable plant reserve is Plantlife's Ranscombe Farm on the North Downs near Strood in Kent, which is deliberately managed along traditional lines and preserves an astonishing range of species, several of which are almost extinct in Britain. Well worth a visit, it demonstrates very clearly what some of the arable fields on South Downs farms must have been like a century or more ago. Would-be time-travellers are also recommended to visit Butser Ancient Farm on the Downs near Petersfield which is a replica of a Bronze Age farm of about 300 BC.

It is not just arable weeds that have taken a hit as modern farming methods have gathered pace. Many interesting plants that once thrived on well-trampled pond margins and in scruffy, neglected corners of old farms have shown spectacular losses.

Farming and nature conservation should not be seen as opposites. A model of wildlife-friendly but still thoroughly commercial farming in the South Downs National Park is provided by Hugh and Chris Passmore, who run Applesham Farm near Lancing. This enterprise of 344 hectares includes high downland and part of the floodplain of the River Adur. It has been farmed by members of the Passmore family for over a hundred years and operates on a traditional mixed rotational system with corn, beef and sheep. The benefits for wildlife are considerable. Corn Buntings, Skylarks and Grey Partridges flourish and a steep bank of permanent chalk grassland supports over one hundred species of plants.

In collaboration with the Game and Wildlife Conservation Trust, the Duke of Norfolk's 1,052 hectares Arundel Estate has recently embarked on an ambitious agri-environmental project, including a major breeding programme for the very scarce Grey Partridge. It has involved turning the huge fields into much smaller fields, divided by hedgerows/beetlebanks and edged by ten metre field headlands. Sensitive crop rotation and sheep grazing have also been key. The aim has been to double the amount of insect food available to ground-nesting chicks like Grey Partridge. The impact has been dramatic. There has been a spectacular increase in Grey Partridges. There are also more than sixty pairs of Corn Bunting, over thirty pairs of Northern Lapwings and four hundred pairs of Skylarks. Arable flowers have flourished including some endangered species. Many mammal species have also benefited from the arable management with more than five hundred Brown Hares recorded in a year.

Hedgerows and trees

Hedgerows are a much-loved feature of the traditional farming landscape. When the first British farmers started clearing the forest to create arable fields and pastures, they left narrow strips of forest to act as boundaries between the clearings. Over the years many of these rews or shaws, as they are termed, have been transformed into hedges. Other hedges have been deliberately planted. Although they may often have started out as single-species hedges, over time they have tended to gain colonist species such as Blackthorn and Elder, and

Postcard by Eric & Norman McCarthy c. 1910

Long-vanished English Elms beside a road in Lancing.

become progressively more species-rich. It has been suggested that the number of woody species in a planted hedge is a rough guide to its age and that by multiplying the number of species in a thirty yard stretch by 110 one obtains an approximate estimate of the age of a hedge.

At one time the Government offered grants for hedge removal. In some places the result has been the creation of an open, prairie-style landscape, conspicuously less rich in wildlife than many urban areas. The reductions in the numbers of farmland birds that used the hedges for nesting have been horrendous. Fortunately the ancient patchwork of small fields with old hedges, shaws and lanes on the clays and sandstones of the South Downs National Park has remained fairly intact in some areas, thanks to sympathetic management.

One of the most striking features in the National Park is the number of oak trees growing in the hedgerows, both Pedunculate Oak on the wetter clays and Sessile Oak on the lighter sandy soils. Without the competition encountered in dense woodlands, these trees can grow into fine specimens. Kipling referred to the 'Huge oaks and old, the which we hold no more than Sussex weed'.

Unfortunately, the magnificent English Elms, which were once an iconic feature of the English countryside, have largely disappeared through the fatal Dutch Elm Disease, a virulent fungal infection imported into Britain in infested logs in the 1970s and spread by the Elm Bark Beetle. For many older naturalists the loss of the tall hedgerow Elms is still a very painful memory. The trees gave great character to the countryside, their distinctive silhouettes adding a vertical scale to the patchwork of fields and trackways. Without their towering presence the landscape feels somehow flatter and less dramatic.

The largest concentration of mature English Elm trees remaining in England is in Brighton and Hove, and in scattered locations between there and Eastbourne. They have survived because of the isolation of the area, between the English Channel and the South Downs, and a tireless campaign by the local authorities and volunteers to identify and remove infected sections of trees within a Dutch Elm Disease Control Area.

Although Elms can be inoculated against the disease it is an expensive and unreliable undertaking. Diseased trees are best cut down and the wood burnt. Suckers often spring up around the stumps but, as they grow up, they in turn become infected and die.

Now, in 2013, we are facing another disaster, with the arrival in the United Kingdom of the fungus *Chalara fraxinea*, which is threatening our native Ash trees. As the Ash is so widespread, its disappearance would have a major impact upon the many other species that are dependent upon it for food and shelter. Ash is often the dominant tree in woods on the Downs, especially where these are self-sown, but it also thrives on heavy clay soils and river floodplains. Late to leaf in the spring, it is one of the first trees to shed its leaves in autumn. Ash trees let through more light than more densely leaved species, such as oaks and Alder, which is why they are often associated with a pleasantly varied ground flora. After the 1987 Great Storm, Ash seedlings were quick to colonise the gaps left in many woodlands where oaks and other trees had fallen.

After the demise of the English Elm, the fear must be that the Ash will be the next tree species to be ravaged by disease and condemned to near oblivion. The ever-changing rural landscape risks once again losing a precious component.

Burton Mill Pond in West Sussex.

The River Valleys and Wetlands

'Water is the source of all life' is a cliché but nevertheless apt. Unpolluted rivers, streams, lakes, water meadows and reed-beds support a huge range of plants and animals, many of which have specialised and exacting ecological requirements. It is not surprising that so many people love to walk along riverbanks or sit gazing across a lake or pond soaking up the tranquil scenes before them. For children too, the highlight of their visits to wildlife education centres is nearly always pond dipping. They are totally absorbed in studying the little creatures they have fished out with their nets.

The South Downs National Park is located in one of the driest parts of the country, but nevertheless it has some important wetland habitats. There are very few lakes (none of any great size), as distinct from ponds which are present almost everywhere. Nor can one find untamed mountain streams or rivers with rocky beds and waterfalls. But seven lowland rivers flow placidly through the Park, each with its own special characteristics and nature conservation value.

Lakes and ponds

At the foot of the South Downs near Petworth is Burton Mill Pond, a 16th-Century hammer pond, which is the one of a very few sites in Sussex for Cowbane. This rare waterside umbellifer is entirely absent from Hampshire. Burton Mill Pond and neighbouring Chingford Pond are good places to watch birds. A small bog close by Burton Mill Pond supports a thriving colony of Cranberry. The lake in Petworth Park is set in beautiful surroundings and is an excellent place to watch Great Crested Grebes performing their elaborate courtship displays from early spring onwards.

Swanbourne Lake near Arundel is fed by chalk springs and held up by a low dam and road causeway. Over-abstraction of groundwater has caused it to dry up in drought years, but attempts are now being made to remedy the problem. One of the interesting aquatic plants that grows at Swanbourne is Marestail. The nearby woods harbour Spurge Laurel, Stinking Hellebore and Box, which may be a native at this location.

Some of the myriads of small ponds that have been dug at various dates in the National Park have acquired very interesting floras and faunas. A newly created pond for example in the Ouse valley near Southease has a fine display of flowering Bladderwort in hot summers. Rootless Duckweed, the world's smallest flowering plant, sometimes turns up in ponds and ditches, but has a habit of disappearing after a few years. A surprising number of small and unremarkable-looking ponds have been found to support breeding colonies of rare Great Crested Newts.

Dew ponds were once widespread on the South Downs, and in the days before piped water supplies shepherds used them as watering places for their sheep. Originally hand dug, they held water because they were lined with cart-loads of clay, fetched in many cases from the Weald. The clay, often mixed with chopped straw, was carefully puddled *in situ* to make it water-tight. The name dew pond is a misnomer; the water they contain comes almost entirely from rain and snow, not dew. Nor is it true that they retain water even in the hottest summers. Kipling's memorable lines,

> 'Only the dew pond on the heights,
> Unfed, that never fails.'

are scientific nonsense. In prolonged droughts even the most resilient dew ponds dry up. However, they have major wildlife value, in good times providing watering places for thirsty animals as well as tiny oases for aquatic and semi-aquatic wildlife. Species inhabiting dew ponds, in general, have to be good dispersers as well as capable of surviving occasional droughts. If not carefully maintained, dew ponds can become choked with vegetation, and also the clay lining can crack or become pierced by plant roots, allowing the water to escape into the underlying chalk. Restoration of some of the more celebrated dew ponds is one of the many challenges facing the new National Park Authority.

© Tony Mundell

Woolmer Pond.

Although lakes are a rarity in the National Park, there is one outstanding example on the heathlands of Woolmer Forest, Woolmer Pond, which is situated on the sandy Folkestone Beds. It is very shallow, and opinion is divided as to whether it is of natural origin or an ancient peat-digging. In Gilbert White's time it was the largest lake in Hampshire, surrounded by open heathland 'without a standing tree on its whole extent'. Later, much of the heathland was planted up with conifers, and the lake itself slowly became infilled with sediment and *Sphagnum* moss. By the end of the 1930s the open water had virtually disappeared. Thanks, however, to clearance and restoration work, particularly by the Army, who use the area for military training, half of the lake has been restored. Especial attention has been paid to re-creating the original sandy bottom of the lake, and to ensuring that, as in Gilbert White's day, the water filling it is only weakly acid and poor in mineral nutrients. Plants such as Shoreweed and Lesser Marshwort now flourish on its margins. Also growing in the area are Marsh St-John's Wort, Marsh Cinquefoil, Small Water-pepper, Hare's-tail Cottongrass and Marsh Clubmoss. The Spangled Water Beetle is found in Britain only at Woolmer Pond and some smaller ponds that have been dug close by.

© Roger Key

Spangled Water Beetle.

Rivers

Chalk is porous and acts as a sponge and so the Downs form a huge reservoir that releases water at a steady rate throughout the year from springs at its junction with underlying non-porous rocks. Rivers that have chalk springs as their source are very special because the chalk also acts as a filter, so crystal-clear water, rich in calcium, emerges. An added advantage is that the temperature of the water issuing from the springs is stable throughout the year, neither hot in summer, nor cold in winter, thus providing a more consistent environment for its aquatic flora and fauna than that in rivers lacking a major groundwater element.

Two of the finest chalk rivers in England are the Hampshire Itchen and its smaller, eastern neighbour the Meon, which rise at the base of the South Downs escarpment and then turn and flow south towards the sea. Both the Itchen and the Meon support breeding populations of Otters, which are slowly returning to many areas of Britain now that they are no longer hunted and waterways are less polluted with pesticides. Strenuous efforts are being made to improve their chances of survival.

Sightings of Otters in the National Park are becoming more frequent.

A pristine distributary of the Itchen at Winnall Moors Nature Reserve.

The River Itchen

The Itchen is well known internationally for its game fishing, largely provided by Brown Trout, both wild and stocked populations. Atlantic Salmon and Sea Trout are mostly sought in the Lower Itchen, south of Winchester. However, its interest extends far wider than its game fish. Its associated valley floor habitats are so important ecologically and support such a wide range of special species that the river has been designated nationally as a Site of Special Scientific Interest over its entire length and internationally as a candidate Special Area of Conservation.

The Itchen flows for 27 miles from its source near Cheriton, passing near New Alresford and then turning south to Winchester and Southampton. Freshwater fills the river for almost its entire length; only the last few miles, which lie outside the National Park, are tidal. Numerous modifications have been made to the river channel over the centuries, such as water-heads for mills and irrigation of the water meadows, which have actually added to the diversity of water habitats rather than destroying them. Alongside the river there are swamp communities, rush pastures, fen meadows, flood pastures and drier grasslands.

Stream Water-crowfoot (*Ranunculus penicillatus* spp. *pseudofluitans*) floats in great rafts on the surface of the fast flowing Itchen, especially in its upper valley. The crowfoot is periodically cleared for fishermen, but still thrives in the clear chalk-laden water. In early sum-

Brown Trout.

© Steve Page/Hampshire & Isle of Wight Wildlife Trust

mer the rafts are spangled all over with small, delicate white flowers. Accompanying the Water-crowfoot are numerous other aquatic plants such as Water Starwort, Watercress and Water Parsnip. Low-growing water-edge plants include Water Forget-me-not and Water Speedwell. Adding to the variety of colour along the water's edge are such taller plants as Yellow Flag, Great Willowherb, Meadowsweet and Purple Loosestrife. The fen meadows and wet meadows provide a rich hunting ground for botanists seeking plants that are particular to those habitats.

Cetti's Warbler.

In some wet areas of the Itchen there are Bulrushes and Reeds. The reedbeds attract nesting Reed Warblers and Sedge Warblers, which can be distinguished by their different songs. The Reed Warblers have low, slow, repetitive calls, whilst the Sedge Warblers have much more varied and busy songs. If one is lucky, one may also find amongst reedbeds and dense vegetation a relatively recent newcomer to Britain: the Cetti's Warbler. A Mediterranean species, it has been gradually spreading northwards in Europe and first bred in Britain in 1972. Hampshire has had more breeding pairs of this species than any other county. One may not see Cetti's Warblers often, as they tend to hide in the vegetation, but the short very loud bursts of their strident calls are unmistakable and the sound carries a very long way.

These wetland habitats can be seen to perfection on the Hampshire & Isle of Wight's superb reserve at Winnall Moors, on the edge of Winchester. Few British cities can boast such a splendid wildlife haven virtually on their doorstep. Well-maintained paths and boardwalks allow the visitor easy access to the reedbeds and former water meadows that constitute the reserve. The Trust has also introduced a grazing regime on traditional lines whereby sheep and cattle live on the downs in the summer and are brought down to graze on some meadows of the Itchen in the winter.

Common Kingfisher.

Winnall Moors meadow with Ragged Robin.

The endangered White-clawed Crayfish.

The female Bullhead attaches her eggs to the underside of stones. The male carefully guards the eggs and later the hatchlings.

The upper Itchen is one of the few remaining locations in lowland Britain for the native White-clawed Crayfish, which feeds on larvae, snails and plants, mainly by night. It has disappeared from most waterways in southern England because an American invader, the introduced Signal Crayfish, has had a devastating impact. It both outcompetes the native species and carries a deadly fungus (popularly known as Crayfish Plague) against which the White-claw has no defence. The Signal Crayfish has not yet invaded the Itchen, but the fungal disease has arrived, perhaps transferred on fish stock, and the White-claw, once widespread in the river, is now confined to a few headwater sites and its future is in doubt.

Over much of its length, the Itchen supports high densities of an interesting but ugly little fish called the Bullhead or Miller's Thumb. A bottom feeder with a large mouth and prominent eyes, it spends much of the day hiding amongst water weed but becomes more active at dusk when it starts to feed. Spurned by fishermen, it has no direct commercial value. Nevertheless it is an important food source for Trout, and for Common Kingfishers and Grey Herons. It is considered to be under threat in many parts of Britain, and is one of the species that justified the Itchen being designated as a Special Area of Conservation.

Another notable resident of the Itchen is the Brook Lamprey. Lampreys are often described as fish, although they lack jaws and a bony skeleton and are members of a seemingly separate and more primitive group of vertebrates, the Agnatha, which are known mostly as fossils. Like the Bull-head, the Brook Lamprey has no sporting or amenity value. Long and thin, it could easily be mistaken for an eel, except that it lacks scales and adults have sucker-like mouths instead of teeth and jaws. The larvae have no eyes or sucker-mouth when they hatch out, and spend the first part of their lives hiding away in the river bed. They eat algae, diatoms and organic debris by filter feeding. When they eventually become adult, they develop a sucker-mouth, but do not attach themselves to other fish and feed on their flesh and body fluids as does the larger and parasitic River Lamprey.

The River Itchen, together with the vegetation bordering much of its course, provides habitats for a wide range of invertebrates including several nationally-rare and scarce species. Over 210 species or groups of species have been recorded from the Itchen itself. The main groups represented are worms, Crustacea (such as the very abundant tiny shrimp-like *Gammarus pulex*), flies and Lacewings. The Ephemeroptera (Mayflies) are strongly represented with nineteen species from six different families. The quality of the chalk river environment is best illustrated by the fact that the maximum numbers of individuals of some of the main groups may reach 4000 per square metre. Given that the water is rich in calcium it is not surprising that there are many aquatic molluscs including the rare Fine-lined Pea Mussel. The terrestrial habitats alongside the river can boast of an equally interesting range of species, such as the tiny Desmoulin's Whorl Snail.

Southern Damselfly.

One of the specially protected rare species for which the Itchen is famous is the Southern Damselfly, which is at the northern limit of its European range. Its normal habitat in the United Kingdom is slow-running acid heathland streams and so it is surprising to find it associated with a chalk river. The relatively warm water in winter is considered to be part of the explanation for its presence here.

The Itchen faces numerous development pressures. Current groundwater abstraction is seriously reducing its flow, watercress beds and fish farms claim a share of the water, and the river is used to dilute treated sewage. Fertiliser runoff, especially phosphates, causes problems particularly in the lower Itchen. In the relatively dry years 1989 to 1992 the flow of the Itchen dropped alarmingly. The Environment Agency works very hard to eliminate these problems.

River Meon with rafts of flowering Water-crowfoot.

The River Meon

This river is in many ways a miniature version of the Itchen. Some would even call it a stream. It rises at springs near the village of East Meon, then flows north and west before turning south to flow through the South Downs to the Solent. Only the final few miles are tidal, and these lie outside the National Park.

The Meon is a shorter river than the Itchen. In dry summers the headwater springs and upper river have been known to dry up (for example in 2009), and the flow regime is much more variable than on the Itchen. Over abstraction of groundwater, particularly for public water supply, remains a problem. Nevertheless, the Meon has many of the special qualities of a typical chalk river or stream, and much useful work is being done by environmental organisations to enhance its biodiversity.

As in the Itchen, the threatened Bullhead and Brook Lamprey are widely distributed. Otters have returned, but not Water Voles, which were last seen in 1989. The voles are believed to have fallen victim to American Mink, which have invaded the whole country since their escape from fur farms. The native Crayfish is also thought to have been lost from the entire river. A major project is currently under way, which aims to reintroduce these lost species and improve the quality of the river.

© Steve Page/Hampshire & Isle of Wight Wildlife Trust

Water Vole.

Brown Trout thrive in the Meon, but there are fears that the Sea Trout, which migrate as far upriver as Warnford, are in decline. Fewer invertebrate species are recorded than on the Itchen, but an impressive number are nationally scarce.

The West Sussex Rother

The River Rother rises just south of Noar Hill near Selborne in Hampshire and flows through the Western Weald for 30 miles before joining the River Arun at Pulborough. It is one of only two rivers in south-eastern Britain with neutral to acid waters and a shifting sandy bottom. Although it rises on chalk, a major tributary joins it from the acid soils of Longmoor Inclosure. Many minor tributaries flow into it from the numerous springs that rise in the valley's Lower Greensand. Unfortunately, there has been a problem in recent years on parts of the Rother where sand has been running off agricultural land into the river.

As with other rivers, many stretches of the Rother are lined with Common Alder, one of our most attractive native trees. Alder has distinctive male catkins, which are purple in winter until opening in the spring, and it is a tree that thrives in wet situations. In boggy ground it is often associated with Downy Birch and Sallow. Alder is particularly noted for its symbiotic relationship with a bacterium which forms nodules on the tree's roots. This nitrogen-fixing bacterium absorbs nitrogen from the air and makes it available to the tree. Fungi that are restricted to Alder include a rare Russula (*Russula pumila*), two milk caps (*Lactarius obscuratus* and *L. cyathula*) and the Alder Roll-rim (*Paxillus filamentosus*). Tragically, a new species of fungus appeared in 1993 which can be fatal for Alders and huge numbers of these trees have died.

© South Downs National Park Authority

West Sussex Rother.

Alder tree and catkins.

On river banks the root systems of the Alder that are exposed in the water give shelter to fish during times of high water flow and provide a safe refuge from predators. The pure waters of the Rother provide an ideal habitat for many species of fish and it is particularly renowned for its Chub, Barbel, Grayling, Brown Trout and Sea Trout. Alder foliage is relatively quick to decompose in water and provides nutrients for invertebrates such as the larvae of caddis flies, and water beetles.

Courtship of Beautiful Demoiselle Damselflies.

A most striking, large damselfly that is found on the Rother is the aptly named the Beautiful Demoiselle. The males have metallic blue-green bodies and dark distinctive wings and the females are also a brilliant metallic green, although their wings have a pale brown suffusion. Their elaborate courtship display and the delicate elegance of their flight are a joy to behold on a hot summer's day. Their natural habitat is clean, fast-flowing, gravel or sandy-bottomed rivers and streams, so they thrive on the Rother.

Otters have not yet re-established themselves as a breeding population on the Sussex rivers, although migrant otters have taken up residence for a while, particularly on the rivers Rother and Arun. One Otter travelled sixty miles from Hampshire only to be electrocuted on a railway line. It is hoped that in time these charismatic animals will once again become a permanent feature of the Sussex waterways.

The Rivers Arun, Adur, Ouse and Cuckmere

The Adur, Ouse and Cuckmere, like the Arun, all rise well to the north of the National Park. Only the lower parts of their valleys where they flow through the South Downs are included within the Park boundary. The Arun in contrast has a sizeable area north of the Chalk outcrop that lies within the Park.

Because all four rivers drain large areas of the Weald before entering the Park much of the water that they carry tends to be acid or neutral in reaction. Within the Park, Chalk groundwater contributes relatively little to their flow (unlike the situation in Hampshire), and as a result the rivers tend to have few water snails, which need plenty of calcium to build their shells. Another salient fact is that the four rivers in their lower courses are tidal. The Cuckmere is tidal up to Milton Lock, just north of Alfriston, and only a very short section within the Park boundary is non-tidal. Both the Ouse and the Adur are tidal quite far into the Weald and well north of the Park boundary. On the Arun, however, the Park boundary and the tidal limit roughly coincide.

The brackishness of the water provides another reason why the four Sussex rivers lack freshwater molluscs in their lower courses. With each tide a wedge of salt water advances up river with the freshwater flow attempting to make its way seaward on top. In theory, the artificially raised river banks confine the saline wedge to the river channel, but in times of flood, if the banks are overtopped, saline water can be deposited on the floodplain. Sluices aided in places by pumps allow rainwater that collects in floodplain ditches to drain into the rivers at low tide, but occasionally the sluices malfunction and salt water from the rivers enters the ditches with calamitous effects on the flora and fauna.

In late Saxon times, Steyning was an important port. The Adur valley to the south was a wide tidal inlet, with a few small villages located along its margins. At low tide a vast expanse of salt marsh and glistening mudflats would have been uncovered, which of course would have disappeared at high water. Over the years the inlet slowly silted up and much of the marshland was reclaimed and converted into pasture. By the end of the Middle Ages New Shoreham had replaced Steyning as the main port on the Adur.

The Ouse valley south of Lewes has had a similar history. It too appears to have been a tidal inlet in late Saxon times, but then began to silt up and was reclaimed. Despite the land reclamation winter flooding was always a problem, and some areas had to be temporarily abandoned. In the Tudor period a new mouth was dug for the Ouse at Newhaven (the river had previously entered the sea at Seaford) and this greatly improved the drainage of the marshland on falling tides, facilitating further land reclamation. As far as can be ascertained the lower Arun and Cuckmere valleys were also once tidal inlets. Arundel like Lewes was a port as well as a market town.

Until the early 1900s the wet pastures or grazing marshes alongside the Arun, Adur, Ouse and Cuckmere were regularly flooded, especially in winter. Now the rivers have been so massively embanked, and their channels so deepened and straightened, that flooding is much less frequent. Old photographs reveal for example that Bramber and Beeding were badly flooded in the winters of 1894, 1904, 1909, 1911, 1924 and 1925; flooding occurs much more rarely now. The frequent flooding and general wetness of the flood-plain grasslands in the early part of the last century attracted large numbers of wintering wildfowl, such as Eurasian Wigeon, as well as Northern Lapwings, Snipe, Redshanks and other waders. Because the ground was so often wet, cattle could be brought onto the fields only comparatively late in the spring, which increased the breeding success of those bird species that stayed to nest and whose eggs were vulnerable to trampling. Now more intensive management and improved drainage has resulted in much heavier livestock grazing and a corresponding reduction in the numbers of wintering and breeding birds. Not only can cattle graze the fields more intensively, but some farmers have seized the opportunity to convert the drier pastures into arable, which further reduces their wildlife value.

No data have been compiled for the National Park, but in Sussex as a whole it is estimated that about 50% of the area of wet grassland that survived in 1960 has now been drained, and in many cases turned over to arable production.

Flowering Water-violet is a welcome sight in May and June.

The historic pastures and grazing marshes are generally thought to have had a great diversity of plants growing on their surfaces, but improved drainage, more intense grazing and the widespread application of fertilisers have greatly reduced the number of species. In the past there would have been drifts of Meadowsweet, Ragged Robin, Marsh Bedstraw and other herbs, but relentless grazing and additions of ferti-liser have produced a monotonous, closely cropped grass sward.

As a result, most of the ecological interest of the floodplain is now restricted to the ditches. Well-maintained ditches harbour a wealth of interesting plants and invertebrates. Two attractive ditch plants that deserve special mention are Flowering-rush and Water-violet. Despite its name, Flow-ering-rush is not a rush, but a tall elegant plant with umbels of attractive pink flowers. Water-violet is an aquatic member of the Primrose family and not a violet. It has submerged feathery leaves and emergent spikes of lilac-coloured flowers. Both species were once more widespread, but have now become quite a rare sight due to poor ditch maintenance and excessive amounts of soil, fertilisers and herbicides washing off fields. The Adur valley remains their main stronghold in Sussex.

Another interesting plant is Frogbit, which floats on the surface of the water in ditches that have not become too overgrown. It has rounded leaves and distinctive three-petalled white flowers, but these set seed only in hot summers and the plant mostly spreads vegetatively by growing offsets.

A rare but beautiful plant that grows best in brackish marshes and the sides of ditches where there are traces of salinity is Marsh Mallow. With its pale pink flowers it is one of the glories of the lower Cuckmere valley. Its roots were prized by herbalists as a source of a medicinal confection, but times have changed and modern marshmallow sweets do not include the plant as an ingredient. A more commonplace and salt-tolerant plant is Sea Aster, which grows on the banks of the Arun and its three eastern neighbours at numerous sites from the sea for many miles inland though not as far as the tidal limits.

Springs from the chalk discharge clean, hard water into some of the ditches on the river floodplains in the central and eastern part of the National Park, thus helping to support a rich mollusc fauna. The Lewes Levels, for example, used to be famous for their rare species of water snail, but the ditches in which they occurred have all too often been allowed to become choked up with vegetation or ruthlessly cleared and several key species have disappeared.

With improved management, much could be done to enhance the wildlife interest of the river floodplains in the central and eastern sections of the National Park. Phosphate and nitrate enrichment from fertilisers needs to be kept to a minimum and ditch clearance needs to be carried out in a careful, controlled manner. A major objective must be to try to prevent ditches from drying out during summer droughts. The efforts of the Knepp Estate to re-wild its floodplain landscape, although outside the National Park, provide a valuable model as to what can be achieved given the necessary motivation.

Reed-beds were doubtless important components of the historic floodplain landscape, but now reeds are mainly confined to the margins of ditches. They still provide valuable habitat for Reed Buntings, Sedge Warblers and other small birds, but what are really needed are more extensive stands of reeds that would interest breeding Bitterns, Marsh Harriers and other species requiring good cover. A tiny reedbed that survives close by the Cuckmere at Litlington provides a glimpse of what could easily be achieved elsewhere by careful re-flooding.

Marsh Mallow. This stately plant is becoming increasingly scarce.

© Tony Mundell

The Arun, Adur and Ouse support a diverse fish fauna. The most celebrated species, the Sea Trout, is a migratory variety of the Brown Trout, closely related to the Atlantic Salmon. The baby trout hatch in tiny tributary streams, such as the Bevern Brook on the Ouse, usually at about Easter time. They spend about 2 to 3 years in fresh water, steadily gaining weight before migrating down river to the sea, usually in spring or early summer. After entering the sea they grow more rapidly than before, and often spend a year or more away, before returning to their home river, often during the summer. They may lurk in the lower reaches of the river for many months before swimming upstream in about the New Year to find a small tributary in which to spawn. After this they typically return to the sea, unlike salmon, which normally die after spawning.

Drainage ditch on Amberley Wild Brooks.

Amberley Wild Brooks and Pulborough Brooks

Looking north from the South Downs Way at Amberley Mount there is an unforgettable view of the Arun winding its way southwards towards the sea. Across the wide Arun gap the chalk downs continue westwards. Below are Amberley Castle and the picturesque village of Amberley. Beyond them are the alluvial grazing marshes and drainage ditches of Amberley Wild Brooks and Pulborough Brooks.

Amberley Wild Brooks have been known to generations of local naturalists as one of the prime wildlife sites in southern England. They have a remarkable concentration of both rare plants and animals. 56% of all British species of water plants, five of the six native amphibians and 42% of our dragonfly species are found amongst these grazing marshes, which are intersected by numerous ditches. One of the most interesting dragonflies is the Scarce Chaser, which is restricted in England to a very few sites in the south-east. Another is the Club-tailed Dragonfly that breeds on the Rother and Arun and only a few other river systems in the country.

The Wild Brooks are a stronghold for Sharp-leaved Pondweed, a very rare protected species, which outside the Arun valley grows mainly in the Pevensey Levels and the Norfolk Broads. Cut Grass is another extreme rarity. Whilst it is found further up the Arun and on a tributary at Shillinglee, its only other British presence is as a re-introduction or possibly as a

The Scarce Chaser dragonfly normally emerges in late May and is mostly confined to river floodplains and water meadows.

native in the Kew/Richmond area. Many a naturalist has regretted handling this well-named plant. At Amberley Wild Brooks it is found in greater abundance than elsewhere. It grows in mud at the water's edge in ditches and seems to benefit from cattle grazing and trampling. It is said to flower only when a warm spring is followed by an even warmer summer. At Amberley and elsewhere in the Arun valley Fine-leaved Water-dropwort, which is quite widely distributed in Britain, is accompanied by its much rarer relative, Narrow-leaved Water-dropwort. Other treasures include Marsh Fern, Small Water-pepper, Climbing Corydalis and Marsh Cinquefoil.

In 1978 the Southern Water Authority published plans to pump drain part of the Brooks 'to enhance the agricultural potential of the land'. The Sussex Wildlife Trust, which had established a nature reserve on the Wild Brooks, led a consortium of local organisations that successfully defeated the proposal through a public inquiry. Since then, the RSPB has acquired Pulborough Brooks and the Sussex Wildlife Trust has extended its own holding on the Wild Brooks and has acquired Waltham Brooks. The two organisations now manage over 530 hectares of these superb wetlands. Several of the rare plants that grow at Amberley are also found at Pulborough Brooks.

© Roger Wilmshurst

A winter gathering of Eurasian Wigeon on Pulborough Brooks.

Further down the Arun the Wildfowl and Wetland Trust's Centre at Arundel has created a wide range of habitats including ponds, reedbeds, fen, wet grasslands and ditches. The Centre is an important sanctuary for Water Voles which were introduced there in 2005 and are now spreading to other sites on the Arun. Another population of this critically endangered species is still hanging on in Pulborough Brooks and Amberley Wild Brooks.

In 2011 these lowland grazing marshes were designated one of three new national Special Areas of Conservation for the Little Whirlpool Ram's-horn Snail. This snail, which lives in the clean, hard waters of ditches on traditionally managed coastal and floodplain grazing marshes, is one of the most protected molluscs in Britain! Not only is it a UK Biodiversity Action Plan (BAP) Priority Species, but it is also a European Protected Species meaning that this endangered snail has the strictest protection across its European range. The waters of the River Arun support another UK BAP Priority Species, the Depressed River Mussel. Nationally important populations of this rather rare mussel lie buried in firm clay sediments along the whole length of river bed within the Park boundary.

In summer, cattle graze the pastures at Amberley and Pulborough, and the ditches are filled with flowers and darting dragonflies. In winter, the wetlands are periodically flooded and become an internationally important home for wintering birds, including Bewick's Swans, several

Short-eared Owl, a scarce winter visitor to the National Park.

© Roger Wilmshurst

thousand Eurasian Wigeon, Eurasian Teal and flocks of sometimes as many as a thousand Northern Lapwing. The magnificent Short-eared Owls, occasional winter visitors mainly from Europe, give huge pleasure to ornithologists as they view them hunting over the rough pastures in daylight. Set against the backdrop of the chalk downs, the Pulborough Brooks, Waltham Brooks and the aptly named Amberley Wild Brooks epitomise all that is special in Britain's newest National Park.

An old Black Poplar at Benbow Pond, Midhurst. The thick furrowed bark and burrs are characteristic of this species.

The Black Poplar was probably once a widespread tree in Britain that grew in floodplain woodlands. It was in great demand because it matured quickly and its wood could be used for many purposes. Over the centuries, the large-scale drainage of the wetlands and measures to prevent flooding have destroyed most of its natural habitat, and the introduction of foreign species, some of which may have hybridised with our native tree, have led to the Black Poplar becoming one of Britain's extremely rare native trees.

A Sussex Black Poplar Working Group set up in 1998 found that there were only 34 mature Black Poplar trees left in Sussex. In collaboration with the Royal Botanic Gardens at Wakehurst Place, cuttings from these trees are now grown as coppice stools and over six thousand Black Poplars have been planted in Sussex river valleys.

Alien pests

River floodplain ecosystems have become particularly prone to invasion by alien pest species, partly because they have been greatly modified by farmers and drainage engineers, and also because of ill-judged introductions. The role of North American Mink and the Signal Crayfish have already been mentioned, but many other invasive species have had a disastrous impact. Parrot's Feather, for example, is a plant that has established itself in many ditches, as has the even more pernicious New Zealand Pygmyweed (also known as Australian Swamp Stonecrop). Fragments of the Pygmyweed easily adhere to fishermen's boots (if not Herons' feet) and so get carried from one site to another, quickly rooting and forming vast mats that smother the indigenous vegetation. Parrot's Feather, a more attractive aquatic from Central America, is often grown in garden ponds, where it can rapidly overcrowd everything else. It is likely that unthinking gardeners have thrown surplus plants into natural watercourses where it easily takes root and spreads. On the Lewes Levels, another pest, the South American water fern, Azolla, often forms floating carpets like Duckweed. It is frost-sensitive and turns red when it dies. Giant Hogweed, a stately introduction from the Caucasus, is spreading rapidly and uncontrollably along the banks of some watercourses. Its sap can cause serious and persistent skin irritation. But perhaps the most troublesome invader is Himalayan Balsam, which is exceedingly pretty when in flower, highly attractive to bees, and has seed pods that explode on touch, delighting children. It spreads inexorably along bank sides and is extremely hard to clear once it has become well-established. Even small fragments quickly take root and become new plants.

The Lewes Levels have become the home of hordes of green Marsh Frogs, a European species that was introduced to the Levels in 1974 from Romney Marsh, where it had been unwisely liberated in 1935 and speedily built up a huge population. Marsh Frogs grow much larger than our native frogs and have toxic skin secretions that deter predators. They are often to be seen sunning themselves on the vegetation at the side of ditches, ready to leap into the water with a loud plop at the first sign of danger. They serenade the night with a rowdy cacophony that sounds embarrassingly lavatorial.

© Robin Crane

© Robin Crane

Himalayan Balsam dominating a river bank.

Birling Gap, the Seven Sisters and Seaford Head at low tide showing the great width of the shore platform.

Coastal Habitats

The South Downs National Park reaches the coast only between Brighton and Eastbourne, and then not everywhere. Newhaven, Seaford and some other coastal settlements lie outside the Park, but the remaining 10.9 miles of coast that fall within the Park include some of the world's finest chalk cliffs and chalk shore platforms. Beachy Head, at the eastern end of the Park, is southern Britain's highest sea cliff. Also within the Park is the estuary of the Cuckmere River, one of the least developed and most natural estuaries in southern Britain.

The National Park boasts an impressive array of coastal habitats including cliff faces and windswept cliff tops, rocky shore platforms and underwater reefs, saltmarsh and shingle beach, but no sand dunes. The plants and animals that have colonised these varied and challenging habitats tend to be highly adapted and specialised in their requirements. Many are nationally scarce, and a select few are of international importance.

Chalk cliffs

The chalk cliffs are retreating ever landwards under the onslaught of the waves, except where they are protected by sea walls. To the east of Brighton the cliff retreat rate averaged about 30–40 cm a year before sea walls were built. The unprotected cliffs of the towering Seven Sisters are exposed to the full force of waves advancing up the Channel and are retreating at an average of 46 cm per year. At Birling Gap the rate rises to over 70 cm a year, but at Beachy Head it falls to only about 8 cm per year on average. Because the chalk cliff faces are in many places being rapidly eroded, plants cannot normally gain much of a foothold. East of Brighton Marina, however, the basally-protected chalk cliff faces have become colonised by such interesting species as the nationally scarce and delightfully fragrant Hoary Stock, which has white or purple flowers. It is regarded by some as doubtfully native, even though it has reputedly been present on the Brighton cliffs for over 200 years. Near Rottingdean it grows alongside a relative of Rock Sea Lavender, which has escaped from cultivation and spread dramatically along the chalk cliffs in recent years, forming conspicuous mauve patches in summer.

During gales, salt-laden winds scour the tops of the chalk cliffs. In the more exposed situations the downland turf has a struggle to establish itself. Only the more resilient species can survive, and those that do are often stunted and prostrate. One would expect the flora to hold little of interest, but actually there are quite a few surprises. Moon Carrot, a great rarity in Britain, and poisonous Henbane grow on Seaford Head, at a place where the cliff top is rather more sheltered than usual. Wall Germander grows on Haven Brow, the first of the Seven Sisters east of Cuckmere Haven. It has endearing pinkish-purple flowers, but is so dwarfed by the wind that hardly anyone passing by ever gives it a second glance, even though this may be the only place in England where it is truly native.

Moon Carrot is found in Britain only at the eastern end of the South Downs and at a very few sites on chalk in East Anglia.

The chalk cliffs are notable for their bird life. A century ago, people regularly climbed down the cliffs to collect the eggs of birds nesting on the ledges. This persecution has now virtually ended, but new hazards have arisen. Paragliders chasing updrafts sometimes glide along the cliff faces causing nesting birds to fly away, leaving their eggs unguarded and vulnerable to crow predation. Abseilers pose an additional hazard. Overall, however, human disturbance is much less than it was. Ravens, which were much persecuted by egg collectors, ceased nesting in Sussex in about 1895, but returned in 2001 to nest on the cliffs at Beachy Head. They have now also colonised some inland cliffs in the National Park. Peregrine Falcons have also resumed cliff breeding, having undergone a catastrophic decline in numbers after ingesting now-banned agricultural pesticides. Kittiwakes started nesting in Sussex in 1976 on the cliffs west of Newhaven, but now nest mainly on the cliffs at the east end of Seaford, where they attract numerous bird watchers. The Kittiwake is the most pelagic of Britain's gulls, generally coming ashore only to breed. After a period of rapid population growth the Sussex birds now seem to be in decline, perhaps because they are finding increasing difficulty obtaining enough food for their chicks. The gull-like Fulmar, which belongs to the Albatross family, is distinguished by its long gliding flights with stiff wings. A few pairs nest on the cliffs, and large flocks can sometimes be seen from the cliffs feeding off shore in the spring.

The coastline serves as an important link with Europe, as it is a staging post for millions of birds and insects migrating to and from the continent every year. As an example, by 2012 ornithologists had recorded a total of 289 different species of birds at Beachy Head as well as about 50 scarce or rare migrants probably diverted from their normal route by unusual weather conditions.

Intertidal zone

As the chalk cliffs retreat they leave behind a gently inclined or stepped platform of chalk at their base. Often a beach of flint shingle masks the junction between the cliffs and the platform. The platform itself is covered in many places by seaweed. Rock pools abound and also runnels or gullies which assist water, thrown up by breaking waves, to flow back into the sea. Chalk shore platforms are home to many interesting plants and animals. The Common Piddock is a bivalve mollusc that uses its hard-edged shell to bore its way into the softer chalk, creating a round hole where it can embed itself. It feeds and breathes with the aid of a siphon that it extends out of the hole. The Common Limpet slowly wears away the chalk as it grazes the algae coating the rock surfaces. It is active only when submerged; when the tide goes out it retreats to its 'home scar', a cup-shaped hollow that it erodes to exactly fit its shell so that it can clamp itself firmly to the rock.

Many species of seaweed grow on the shore platforms, such as the Serrated Wrack. Seaweed fronds are a favourite hiding place for periwinkles and other shore animals. On the lower platforms, which are frequently submerged by the tide, Beadlet Anemones, Purse Sponges, chitons, barnacles and crabs are common. The runnels and the platforms extend out under the sea for considerable distances beyond the low-water mark. Permanently submerged are chalk reefs that attract shoals of fish and other forms of marine life, including two species of seahorse. East of Beachy Head, the chalk gives way to sandstone, which forms a series of submerged rocky ridges and gullies, again rich in marine life.

Because of their exceptional biodiversity, the intertidal shore platforms and the near-shore sea bed between Seaford and Eastbourne have been designated as the Seven Sisters Voluntary Marine Conservation Area. Following Parliamentary approval for the new Marine Bill part of this area (and an extension further west to Brighton) is expected to receive full statutory protection. Trawling and similarly destructive forms of fishing will be banned, allowing fish stocks to improve and stopping further damage to the sea bed. The protected area will extend from the low-water mark out to sea for a distance of just under a kilometre, well beyond the boundary of the National Park, which is at mean low-water mark, except at Telscombe where it follows the cliff edge.

The meanders of the lower Cuckmere no longer connect with the river.

Lower Cuckmere Valley

The lower Cuckmere valley is remarkably unspoilt, and a highlight of the National Park. The port and town of Newhaven at the mouth of the Ouse only a few kilometres to the west are a reminder of what could easily have been the fate of Cuckmere Haven if developers and industrialists had moved in. That they did not do so must be seen as something of a miracle. It would be wrong, however, to describe the Cuckmere estuary as totally in a state of nature. In 1846–47 the 'New Cut' was dug to bypass the elegant meanders of the Cuckmere near Exceat Farm, allowing barges better access to Alfriston and landowners further opportunities to drain the mud flats and salt marshes. The latter are now grazing marsh, but the former salt marsh creeks form slight depressions in the surface that are very obvious from the air. The meanders survive but are now totally cut off from the river and form a saline lagoon, which is in danger of silting up. Strenuous efforts have been made to keep the river mouth in its present position on the west side of the valley. Historically, it has wandered from one side to the other. At the end of the First World War, for example, it lay on the east side, under Haven Brow. The Environment Agency has put forward a controversial plan to reconnect the meanders to the river and let the grazing marshes flood at high tide, returning them to salt marsh. The man-made retaining banks along the river, which may in part date back to mediaeval times, will be allowed to fall into disrepair, letting floodwater onto the marshes wherever breaches occur. This 'back to nature'

Glasswort tolerates prolonged submergence by the tide.

© Barry Yates/Sussex Wildlife Trust

and low-cost approach has won much support but has provoked the wrath of many local residents as well as visitors from far afield, who wish to see the landscape preserved as it is.

Between the river and its retaining banks are areas of salt marsh that are uncovered at low tide but hidden when the tide rises. At one time there would have been wide expanses of bare mud, rather than marsh. Glasswort or, as it is sometimes called, Marsh Samphire would have soon colonised the mud, helping to stabilise it. This annual is exceptionally salt-tolerant and quick growing. Its swol-

len erect stems would have trapped mud brought in on each tide, and its shallow roots would have bound the mud, reducing tidal scour. As the mud gradually accumulated the surface of the Cuckmere salt marsh would have become raised and the Glasswort, submerged for ever-shorter periods, would have become crowded out by Sea Purslane. This bushy perennial, which has flattened grey-green leaves and a strong root system, dominates the existing salt marsh, except where creeks and salt pans have developed. The Glasswort survives only low down on the marsh where the Purslane struggles to gain a foothold.

© Neil Fletcher/Sussex Wildlife Trust

The ditches around the grazing marshes of the lower Cuckmere valley are of considerable botanical interest and include the elegant Flowering-rush, which has rosy pink flowers and sword-shaped leaves.

Over time the Purslane traps still more mud, and as the surface becomes ever more raised, the salt marsh is less and less frequently submerged. Sea Wormwood and Sea Aster appear, marking a further stage of salt-marsh development. They are flooded on only the highest tides.

The lower Cuckmere valley is celebrated for its bird life. Many waders and water fowl are attracted to the river meanders and the saline lagoon known as 'The Scrape' that has been excavated north of the beach and its adjacent shingle area. The Scrape, which dates from 1975, is a replacement for an earlier lagoon that was present early in the last century, and formed, possibly entirely naturally, as a result of changes in the position of the mouth of the Cuckmere. The bird life is particularly interesting during spring and autumn migrations, when sometimes such rarities as Spoonbills stop over and use the area for feeding. Unfortunately, relatively few species remain to breed. As a result of human disturbance and predation by Carrion Crows and Foxes, species such as Ringed Plover, Northern Lapwing and Redshank no longer nest in the lower Cuckmere valley on a regular basis. Artificial shingle islands have been created within The Scrape lagoon and in theory ought to attract nesting plover, if only fox and crow predation and pressure from human visitors could be reduced. Canada Geese congregate on the marshes, especially in winter, cropping the turf alongside other water fowl, notably migratory Eurasian Wigeon.

Shingle

The beach of flint shingle at the mouth of the Cuckmere is apparently slowly being built outwards into the Channel. On the landward side of the strandline a wide strip of shingle now lies beyond the reach of the waves, and has been colonised by an interesting community of pioneer plants that have to endure salt spray and high winds, as well as all too little soil and periodic desiccation. One of the most conspicuous species is the nationally scarce Sea Kale, a relative of the cabbage, which has a very strong tap root that can reach down as much as two metres through the shingle in search of fresh water. Its first shoots in spring are a striking purplish-blue, but as they age they enlarge and become glaucous green with a waxy coating that is water repellent and reduces transpiration. The mound-like clusters of creamy white flowers are a magnificent sight in June and July. Other perennials growing on the shingle at Cuckmere Haven include Sea Beet, a relative of spinach beet with shiny, dark green leaves,

The shingle beach at Cuckmere Haven with Sea Kale and Yellow Horned-poppy colonising its landward margin.

Yellow Horned-poppy is quick to colonise shingle beaches beyond the reach of the tide.

and the handsome Yellow Horned-poppy which has a deep tap root and leaves covered with downy hairs to restrict water loss. With its deep yellow flowers, the poppy stands out in summer as a splash of colour against the grey flint shingle. Its long curved seed pods hold thousands of tiny seeds, which are usually dispersed by the wind but can also float on sea water. Also colourful is Red Valerian, which is not a native and has possibly escaped from the gardens of the former Coastguard Cottages. Easily missed is the diminutive Sea-milkwort, whose tiny pink flowers reveal it to be a member of the primrose family. Like many plants it hugs the shingle, forming low-growing mats.

The plants on the shingle eke out a precarious existence. Sea-holly was described as plentiful at Cuckmere in 1851, but is now no longer to be found. Perhaps it succumbed to trampling, or was picked out of existence. Sea Kale, by contrast, has made a spirited recovery since 1937 when it was recorded as rare. One wonders how long the plants of the shingle will survive as global warming continues and sea levels rise. The species that presently struggle for survival at Cuckmere Haven face an uncertain future, and have deservedly become the focus of conservation efforts. Vegetated shingle is a rare habitat globally and it is important to try to conserve it wherever it occurs.

The glaucous leaves and imposing seed heads of Sea Kale.

Only by getting close to nature do children learn to love and respect it. Only when we respect nature will we learn to treat it well.

The Future

The plant and animal populations within the South Downs National Park are in a constant state of flux. Species at or near the northern edge of their range are particularly affected by abnormal weather conditions. In the hot summer of 2009 many tens of millions of Painted Lady butterflies migrated to Britain from southern Europe and North Africa. This beautiful species lays its eggs on thistles after arriving in Britain, in hot years in very great numbers, but it has yet to become a permanent resident because the winters are too cold.

There is increasing evidence that global warming is leading to greater climatic instability. Unusual weather conditions look set to become more usual. Higher temperatures can increase the frequency of droughts, but warmer air can also hold more moisture. When rain falls it can turn into a deluge and trigger floods with major consequences not only for humans but also for wildlife. Because the weather is becoming more unsettled the plants and animals of the National Park face an increasingly uncertain future. Of course there will be gains to celebrate as well as losses that may be very regrettable. The Little Egret is a small, elegant white heron that fifty years ago bred no further north than southern Europe and was known in Britain only as a very rare vagrant. It is now resident in many southern counties and is often to be seen in the National Park fishing in ponds and ditches. As the climate continues to warm,

© Robin Crane

Little Egret have become a familiar sight in southern England.

the Purple Heron and Cattle Egret can be expected to follow the example of the Little Egret and start breeding in Britain on a permanent basis. It is an encouraging thought but unfortunately for every species gained there are currently several losses because of climatic change or habitat alteration either in Britain or along migration routes. Already we have lost the Wryneck and Red Backed Shrike as regular breeding species in Britain and the Willow Tit and Lesser Spotted Woodpecker look set to follow.

Species are still disappearing at an alarming rate despite everything that is being done to protect their habitats and enhance their chances of survival. We can be justifi-

ably proud of all the research that is being carried out to try to discover the precise needs of individual threatened species, but there is much that is still not understood. Just why, for example, are the Willow Tit and Lesser Spotted Woodpecker in trouble? The closely related Marsh Tit and Great Spotted Woodpecker continue to flourish. The subtleties of species' requirements take a lot of unravelling. The elegant White Admiral butterfly is a good example. As has long been known, caterpillars of this species feed solely on Honeysuckle. Recent research has established that the female butterflies lay their eggs only on the most straggly shoots of Honeysuckle in semi-shade. For some reason

© Neil Hulme

The majestic White Admiral, an unmistakeable woodland butterfly.

The future of the countryside and wild places within the National Park is dependent on the support of farmers who are willing to manage their land sympathetically despite the economic challenges that lie ahead. Green consumerism can play a part in securing conservation objectives, but only at the margins. It is essential that non-governmental organisations such as the Wildlife Trusts, the RSPB and the National Trust scale up their efforts to save Britain's natural heritage and to persuade Government to take wildlife more seriously. Huge efforts have been made over the years by dedicated organisations and individuals to conserve and enhance the wildlife and habitats within the South Downs National Park, but nature never stands still. It will be fascinating to follow the changes that will inevitably take place in the future. The new National Park Authority has come into being at a critical time, and will no doubt face many challenges. It deserves the support of everyone who is concerned to create a more wildlife-friendly environment within its boundaries. Let us hope that this and later generations will be able to echo Gilbert White's words of 1789 in his Natural History and Antiquities of Selborne and feel as richly rewarded as he was:

'Though I have now travelled the Sussex Downs upwards of thirty years, yet I still investigate that chain of majestic mountains with fresh admiration year by year; and think I see new beauties every time I traverse it.'

lush masses of flowering Honeysuckle in open, sunny situations are ignored. This egg-laying behaviour of the female butterflies has major implications for woodland management. Short-rotation coppicing favours fritillaries but not the White Admiral, which requires undisturbed and fairly mature woodland.

What will happen to the White Admiral in Britain as global warming intensifies? We already know that in hot summers bird predation is minimised because the caterpillars grow quickly and the chrysalises take only a short time to mature. During cool summers birds exact a much heavier toll. We may guess therefore that global warming is likely to benefit this particular species. Many others, however, will be less lucky.

How to find out more about the natural history of the South Downs National Park

Some Places to Visit

WOODLANDS

Ebernoe Common and Butcherlands	Sussex Wildlife Trust	SU 980271	Ancient wood pasture, dominated by Oak in the north and Beech in the south where the soil is more acidic. The site has long been noted for its rare fungi, lichens and bats. Wild Daffodils and Greater Butterfly Orchids flourish in parts of the woodland, and areas of scrub attract breeding Nightingales. Furnace Meadow (a Plantlife Reserve) boasts a rich grassland flora and Furnace Pond has interesting dragonflies. Former arable land (Butcherland) is being reverted to woodland.
The Mens	Sussex Wildlife Trust	TQ 023235	Huge ancient woodland reverting to a wild state.
Kingley Vale	Natural England	SU 21117	Finest Yew wood in Europe, chalk grassland and scrub. Small areas of chalk heath. Fallow and Roe Deer. Birds including wintering thrushes.
Rewell Wood	Norfolk Estate	SU 983085	Large woodland complex with Sweet Chestnut coppice, Beech plantation and woodland rides with many species of butterflies and moths.
Rook Clift	Private ownership	SU 819183	Wood with ancient Large-leaved Lime and Solomon's Seal. Access limited to public footpath.
Chappetts Copse	Hampshire & Isle of Wight Trust	SU 653234	Beech wood with ancient woodland species such as Solomon's Seal and Woodruff. Orchids including the largest colony of Narrow-leaved Helleborine in England.
Alice Holt Forest	Forestry Commission	SU 810420	382 ha ancient woodland, coppice, wet woodland and forest streams. Roe and Muntjac Deer. Managed for Purple Emperor and other woodland butterflies. Diverse recreational facilities.
Ashford Hangers	Hampshire County Council	SU 740268	One of Hampshire's most beautiful woodland areas, where the poet Edward Thomas lived. The site with its rich mix of habitats on the steep slopes of the Chalk and Upper Greensand is noted for its rare plants.

CHALK GRASSLANDS

St Catherine's Hill	Hampshire & Isle of Wight Trust	SU 484276	Iron Age hill fort. Flower-rich grassland. Brown Argus, Autumn Lady's Tresses.
Old Winchester Hill	Natural England	SU 640205	Iron Age hill fort. One of the richest botanical sites in southern Britain. Round-headed Rampion, Juniper scrub and Yew woodland.
Beacon Hill, Warnford	Natural England	SU 603227	Outstanding for chalk grassland species including Common Rock-rose, Scabious, Yellow Rattle, Round-headed Rampion and Field Fleawort. 25 species of breeding butterfly. Different aspects from east by south round to north give rise to a variety of vegetation types.
Noar Hill	Hampshire & Isle of Wight Trust	SU 742319	Medieval chalk workings. Grassland with Juniper and Box. Rich Orchid flora including Musk and Frog Orchids. Butterflies include Duke of Burgundy and Brown Hairstreak.

CHALK GRASSLANDS (cont.)

Castle Hill	Natural England	TQ 376064	Early Spider Orchid, Nottingham Catchfly, Field Fleawort, Wart-biter Bush Cricket and Great Green Bush-Cricket.
Malling Down	Sussex Wildlife Trust	TQ 427110	Adonis Blue, Silver-spotted Skipper, Forester Moths and Chalk Milkwort.
Mount Caburn	Natural England	TQ 445088	Orchid-rich chalk grassland and scrub. Largest British population of Burnt-tip Orchid. Bronze Age hill fort.

CHALK HEATH

Lullington Heath	Natural England	TQ 545017	Acid heathland plants such as Ling, Bell Heather and Slender St John's Wort growing together with Dropwort, Salad Burnet and Common Milkwort.
Windover Hill	Access Land	TQ 543033	Small area of typical chalk heath and excellent chalk grassland in adjacent Deep Dene, with Grayling and Silver-spotted Skipper.

HEATHLAND

Shortheath Common	Hampshire County Council	SU 775367	Mire and quaking bog with Frogbit, Bladderwort, Narrow-leaved Arrowhead and largest colony of Cranberry in southern England. Large pond, Oak and Birch woodland.
Iping, Stedham and Trotton Commons	Sussex Wildlife Trust	SU 850220	Excellent public access to a whole range of heathland habitats. Woodlark, Tree Pipit, Dartford Warbler, Nightjar and Great Spotted Woodpecker. Silver-studded Blue, Field Cricket, dragonflies, spiders, wasps and beetles.
Lavington Common	National Trust	SU 940188	Dry and wet heathland habitats. Excellent for spiders. An Orb Web Spider which weighed 2.25 g was heaviest spider recorded in Britain.
Ambersham Common	Access Land	SU 913197	Raised bog and an extensive area of wet heath. Good for heathland birds. Sand Lizards.
Chapel Common	Access Land	SU 812282	Excellent access to predominantly dry heathland with Silver-studded Blues.

RIVERS AND WETLANDS

Winnall Moors	Hampshire & Isle of Wight Trust	SU 486297	Outstanding site on the Itchen with chalk stream, tall fen, hay meadow and wet pasture habitats. Plant life includes Green-flowered Helleborine and Southern Marsh Orchid. Birds include Little Grebe, Cetti's Warbler, Reed and Sedge Warblers.
Amberley Wild Brooks	Sussex Wildlife Trust	TQ 027146	Spectacular and rare wetland plants and insects, especially dragonflies. Public access is restricted to the Wey South Path, which runs through the middle of the Brooks directly north from Hog Lane in the village of Amberley.
Lower Cuckmere valley	East Sussex County Council & others	TV 995618	Riverside pastures, ditches, downland and forest.

COASTAL

Beachy Head Seven Sisters Seaford Head	Eastbourne Council National Trust East Sussex CC Seaford DC		These three areas are grouped together because they are in close proximity and are of outstanding national importance for their Chalk cliffs, chalk grasslands, coastal and marine habitats.

Some Places to Visit *(cont.)*

MISCELLANEOUS

Woods Mill Small Dole Henfield BN5 9LE	Sussex Wildlife Trust		Headquarters of the Sussex Wildlife Trust and a nature reserve with a lake, streams, woodland, reedbeds and meadows. The Mill buildings are not open to the public.
Queen Elizabeth Country Park Petersfield PO8 0QE	Hampshire County Council		Includes Butser Hill National Nature Reserve. The Park consists of improved and unimproved calcareous grassland with scattered scrub, Yew woodland and broadleaved woodland. The site has a very rich bryophyte and lichen flora with over 200 lichen, moss and liverwort species being recorded in the chalk grassland. As the highest point on the chalk downland within the National Park, Butser Hill dominates the surrounding landscape. A large area is designated as a Scheduled Ancient Monument reflecting its historical significance, particularly in the Iron and Bronze Ages.
Pulborough Brooks Reserve RH20 2EL	RSPB		In winter flooded meadows teem with ducks, geese and swans. In spring, wading birds, such as Northern Lapwings and Redshanks, breed amongst the pools and ditches, and Nightingales sing from the hedgerows. A heathland restoration project is already attracting Woodlarks and Nightjars.
Seven Sisters Country Park Seaford BN25 4AD	East Sussex County Council		Visitor Centre, educational facilities and country park. Superb coastal views, chalk grasslands and marine habitats.
Arundel Wetland Centre, Mill Road, Arundel, Sussex BN18 9PB	Wildfowl and Wetlands Trust		As well as having a collection of ducks and geese, a wide range of habitats has been created with ponds, reedbeds, fen, wet grasslands and ditches.
Gilbert White Museum and Oates Collection High Street Selborne GU34 3JH			The Wakes, Gilbert White's former home is now a fine, small museum. The gardens that White laid out are carefully maintained.

Websites

www.southdowns.gov.uk – South Downs National Park Authority is the body whose statutory duties are to conserve and enhance the natural beauty, wildlife and cultural heritage of the area and to promote opportunities for the understanding and enjoyment of the special qualities of the Park by the public.

www.naturalengland.org.uk – Natural England is the Government agency responsible for nature conservation, National Nature Reserves, rare species protection and funding of incentive schemes.

www.nationaltrust.org.uk – Owns and manages nature reserves and outstanding countryside sites in the South Downs National Park.

www.sussexwildlifetrust.org.uk and **www.hwt.org.uk** – The Sussex Wildlife Trust and the Hampshire & Isle of Wight Trust own and manage nature reserves and deliver wider countryside and marine conservation. They speak out on local conservation issues and run extensive educational programmes.

www.sxbrc.org.uk – The Sussex Biodiversity Record Centre is the repository, custodian, manager and interpreter of high-quality biodiversity and environmental information for Sussex. Data are welcomed from conservation organisations and individual naturalists. The Centre is managed by the Sussex Wildlife Trust on behalf of Sussex Local Authorities and conservation organisations.

www.hants.gov.uk/biodiversity/hbic – Hampshire biological records centre is a partnership hosted by Hampshire County Council similar to the Sussex Biological Records Centre.

www.rspb – Royal Society for the Protection of Birds speaks out on behalf of birds. Manages Pulborough Brooks and runs education projects.

www.arc-trust.org – Amphibian and Reptile Conservation Trust.

www.plantlife.org.uk – Plantlife.

www.wwt.org.uk – Wildfowl and Wetlands Trust.

www.hantsiow-butterflies.org.uk – Hampshire & Isle of Wight branch of Butterfly Conservation.

www.hantsplants.org.uk – Hampshire branch of Botanical Society of the British Isles.

www.hos.org.uk – Hampshire Ornithological Society.

www.sussexflora.org.uk – Sussex Botanical Recording Society.

www.sussex-butterflies.org.uk – Sussex branch of Butterfly Conservation.

www.sos.org.uk – Sussex Ornithological Society.

www.woodlandtrust.org.uk – Woodland Trust.

Bibliography

Abraham, F. & Rose, F. (2000) Large-leaved Lime on the South Downs. *British Wildlife* 12: 86–90.

Arscott, D. (1994) *Living Sussex*. Lewes: Pomegranate Press.

Belden, P., Downer V.J., Luck, J.C., Prendergast, H.D.V. & Sadler, D. (2004) *The Dragonflies of Sussex*. Essedon Press.

Brandon, P. (1998) *The South Downs*. Chichester: Phillimore & Co.

Brewis, A., Bowman, P. & Rose, F. (1996) *The Flora of Hampshire*. Harley Books.

Briggs, M. (2001) *The Sussex Rare Plant Register*. Sussex Botanical Recording Society.

Briggs, M. (2004) *Sussex Wild Flowers*. Sussex Wildlife Trust.

Brooks, S. & Lewington R. (1997) *Dragonflies and Damselflies of Great Britain and Ireland*. British Wildlife Publishing.

Chatters, C. (2010) *Wild Hampshire & Isle of Wight*. Hampshire & Isle of Wight Trust.

Coulcher, P. (2001) *Unto the Hills – the History and Wildlife of the South Downs*. Lewes: The Book Guild.

Crane, R. (2011) The South Downs National Park. *British Wildlife* 23: 77–88.

Edmonds, H.A. (2012) Lapwings on a downland farm. *British Wildlife* 23: 186–93.

Gibbons, H.W., Reid, J.B. & Chapman, R.A. (1993) *The New Atlas of Breeding Birds in Britain & Ireland: 1988–1991*. BTO, Poyser.

Haes, E.C.M. (1977) *Natural History of Sussex*. Flare Books.

Hall, P.C. (1980) *Sussex Plant Atlas*. Brighton Borough Council, Booth Museum of Natural History.

Hampshire & Isle of Wight Trust (2001) *Wildlife and Wild Places*.

Hampshire Ornithological Society (2010) *Annual Report 2010*.

Horsham Natural History Society (1977) *Natural History of The Mens, Sussex*.

Hudson, W.H. (1903) *Hampshire Days*.

Hudson, W.H. (1923) *Nature In Downland*.

James, P. (1996) *Birds of Sussex*. Sussex Ornithological Society.

Jenkinson, M.N. (1995) *Wild Orchids of Hampshire and the Isle of Wight*. Stour Provost, Dorset: Orchid Sundries Ltd.

Lang, D. (2001) *Wild Orchids of Sussex*. Lewes: Pomegranate Press.

Marren, P. & Rothschild, M. (1997) *Rothschild's Reserves*. Harley Books.

Mortimer, D. (2008) *A Sussex Guide - Sussex Wildlife*. Snake River Press.

Peterken, G. (1981) *Woodland Conservation and Management*. Chapman & Hall.

Preston, C.D., Pearman, D.A. & Dines, T.D. (2002) *New Atlas of the British Flora*. Oxford University Press.

Rackham, O. (1976) *Trees and Woodland in the British Landscape*. J M Dent .

Rackham, O. (2008) *Woodlands*. (New Naturalist Series) London: Collins.

Rand, M. & Mundell, T. (2011) *Hampshire Rare Plant Register*. Privately Published.

Rose, F. (1999) Indicators of ancient woodlands. *British Wildlife* 10: 241–51.

Smart, G. & Brandon, P. (2007) *The Future of the South Downs*. Chichester: Packard Publishing.

Streeter, D. & Garrard, I. (1983) *The Wildflowers of the British Isles*. Midsummer Books.

Sussex Ornithological Society *Annual Reports*.

Sussex Wildlife Trust (1996) *A Vision for the South Downs*.

Thomas, J. & Lewington R. (2010) *The Butterflies of Britain and Ireland*. British Wildlife Publishing.

Walpole Bond, J. (1938) *A History of Sussex Birds*. Witherby.

Webb, N. (1986) *Heathlands*. (New Naturalist Series) London: Collins.

White, G. (1789) *The Natural History of Selborne*.

Williamson, R. (1978) *The Great Yew Forest*. Macmillan.

Wooldridge, S.W. & Goldring, F. (1953) *The Weald*. (New Naturalist Series) London: Collins.

Woolmer Forest Conservation Group (2006) Woolmer Forest: 30 years of conservation work. *British Wildlife* 17: 185–93.

Index